1. The scene is in the Eastern Sudan: the 'buckets' of goat-skin each took about half an hour to fill with perhaps a gallon of water. The time is the dry season, the *sef*. The place has the same mean annual rainfall as London but all of it falls in four or five months. There is no rain *at all* at other times. This illustrates vividly the effect of limited seasonal rainfall.

Water, Weather and Prehistory

by Robert Raikes

With a Foreword by SIR MORTIMER WHEELER

Humanities Press Inc
303 PARK AVENUE SOUTH
NEW YORK, N.Y.

First published 1967 by
John Baker Publishers Ltd.
5 Royal Opera Arcade
Pall Mall, London,
S.W.1

Humanities Press Inc
303 Park Avenue South
New York, N.Y.

Library of Congress Catalog Card No: 67–23022

PRINTED IN GREAT BRITAIN AT
THE UNIVERSITY PRESS
ABERDEEN

Foreword

by Sir Mortimer Wheeler

How clever we all were, we archaeologists, a generation or more ago! At last we were emerging from protoplasmic simplicity and were beginning to understand. We were all becoming Scientists and we had our problems on the run. For example, we had Climate nicely ordered in clear successive phases and attractively labelled with romantic names such as Boreal and Atlantic. We had pollen-analysis, nowadays disguised as palynology, which told us about ancient climates and environments with reference to dominant plant-growths, as revealed by the more or less fortuitous survival of seeds in peat-bogs and other sympathetic soils. A ruined town or a derelict field-system marooned in a desert proved, for all to see, a change of climate within the past 4,000 or even 2,000 years. How could it be otherwise? The Races of Man were neatly docketed under a series of fantastic sobriquets with equally fantastic geographical implications. Of course, all this and more was merely a rebirth or enlargement of an old habit. There was a time—and it goes back far behind Thomsen of Copenhagen—when we thought of human Progress in terms of successive Ages of Stone, Bronze, Iron. There was even a time, I believe, when we sought to cram ethics into ten incontrovertible commandments.

This habit of Classification. Let it be written in letters of brass over every study-door: Classification is Fossilisation. It is the petrifaction of organic thinking, of that mobile and tireless *curiosity* from which discoveries spring. True, one merit can be conceded to classification; it symbolises the importance attached at the time to that which is classified. So much, so good; but for the rest it is, or should be, a challenge to disbelief and renewed search, not, as it too often is, a cushion for satisfaction.

The present book is, in the first place, just such a challenge to what may be called the archaeological establishment. It challenges established belief in recurrent 'changes of climate', the imprecise usage of terms such as 'wetter', 'drier', 'warmer', 'more genial': 'wetter', etc. than what? It discusses evidences of desiccation or flooding in the light of all the circumstances, human and natural, which can reasonably be brought to bear; and again and again the evidence is explicable in terms, not of basic climatic change, but in those of human adequacy or inadequacy in the face of the inherent variability of rainfall with its consequences, and of human improvidence expressed by over-grazing, extravagant tree-felling, faulty engineering (including maintenance), and the like. Insisting upon the visualisation of climate as an integral world-wide problem without geographical boundaries, the author finds no significant 'change of climate' within the past 9,000 years or so; roughly, as it happens, since Man began to turn the tables upon environment, and often enough to make a pretty good mess of it.

But if Man is usually the sinner in these matters, Mr Raikes as a hydrologist is prepared also to admit natural causes of disaster, and cites instances. Thus his analysis of recent probings suggests that the notorious Sybaris in southern Italy was in fact drowned by catastrophic subsidences accompanied in at least one instance by a tidal wave. At Mohenjo-daro, the great chalcolithic metropolis which flourished in Sind (West Pakistan) about 2000 B.C., a series of extraordinarily deep flood-deposits laid down in still water between successions of occupation-layers is provisionally ascribed to a tectonic uplift, or series of uplifts, along the Makran coast (where ancient beaches and formerly coastal sites now lie inland) and somewhere between Mohenjo-daro and the present coastline, thus ponding back the accumulating floods of the Indus system, and from time to time drowning much of the great city. Here, if this hypothesis be correct as it well may be, Man was not the only causative factor; and several inferences of high archaeological importance depend from the postulate.

In all these and many more instances, no small part of the solution lies in a study of water and its variable content, of hydrology—always considered, of course, in relation to many other factors. Hydrology has begun at last to claim its proper place in the equipment of the compleat archaeologist. And here, opportunely, is an introductory handbook to the subject. Mr Raikes describes his science as 'a comparatively recent addition to the large range of applied sciences'. In the far-reaching study of Man it is still indifferently understood. The poet, as is the way of poets, had a flash of understanding far ahead of the scientists when, more than two dozen centuries ago, he proclaimed 'Water is Best'. At least, with more than a gesture of friendship to the author, I regard it as a duty to introduce this essential new book on water to those of my persuasion who are young (or old) enough to learn.

Contents

List of Illustrations

Author's Preface

When anyone writes a book for the first time and when he chooses a subject that involves going outside his own probably limited disciplinary boundaries the question is inevitably asked: Why? It is not only a fair question but one that has to be answered convincingly if the author's views are to carry conviction.

I am a hydrologist and became one through the same kind of accidental series of events that eventually led to recognition of the links between my profession and archaeology. Despite a fascination with water that started at a very tender age, I might never have become a hydrologist if I had not been sent, as a punishment for having spoken my mind with more frankness than discretion about what appeared to me to be a rather scandalous state of affairs, to a remote semi-desert station, to prepare and carry out water development projects. It would not be an exaggeration to say that when I went there I knew nothing whatever about hydrology. When I left after four exciting years of absorbing interest, I had taught myself enough to realise that I still knew very little and had only taken the first halting steps in a process of learning which is still a very long way from being complete. In fact it will never be complete, because hydrology is a young, healthy and growing science the horizons of which are always out of reach. But I had embarked on a way of earning my living of such fascination that I have never since thought of it as 'work', even when—as happens frequently—it occupies far more than a normal working day. So a fascination born of legitimate trout fishing with occasional incursions into the much more difficult business of tickling trout (in parenthesis one wonders why anything so highly skilled and essentially fair as tickling should be considered illegal) found practical expression. It was nurtured by a love of small rivers for their own beauty, and by the discovery that army boots were more bearable on absurdly long cross-country training marches if well soaked by wading at every opportunity in puddles, streams, and ditches; and even survived a commando instructor's request (I want two volunteers, you and *you*, pointing at me) to swim in the nude in February in the Caledonian Canal.

The semi-desert station, where my daily ration of water was twenty gallons for all purposes, delivered from goatskin bags on a donkey, brought home fairly sharply to one already in love with water the problems of those who lack it.

It was at about this time that an archaeological friend introduced me to the remains of abandoned towns, while a journey into the Libyan desert and the discovery of quern stones and potsherds at considerable distances from wells and intermittent sources of water set me wondering how primitive people had survived under such conditions. From there I moved to Baluchistan, a quite different kind of semi-desert, and was immediately introduced to Professor Stuart Piggott's book on *Prehistoric India*. My work took me to many seldom visited places and along rarely used tracks, and almost everywhere there were mounds or *tells* as evidence of people who had lived there thousands of years before. Piggott relied heavily on the authoritative opinions of Sir Aurel Stein who was convinced that Buluchistan had once enjoyed a wetter climate and had entered a long phase of desiccation that was still continuing. I was concerned with proposals for the better use of such little water as is now available from rain, springs, underground supplies and occasional small rivers and a question arose immediately: Was development worth the money and effort if Stein's views were right? After a year or so during which my travels covered almost every place which Stein had visited and quite a number that he had not, I studied his evidence again, and his and Piggott's deductions from it, and concluded that the desiccation theory was untenable on the evidence adduced. This is not to say that desiccation has not occurred, but rather that the evidence seemed to show that the climatic conditions of chalcolithic times had been about the same as those of today.

This all led to a decisive step that I never regretted except during the few weeks of uncertainty that followed it. I wrote to Piggott, in a long and rather argumentative letter, giving him many of my reasons for disagreeing with him and Stein. Two things happened. Firstly I received a letter from a lady then unknown to me—Miss Beatrice de Cardi, who was planning her 1956 expedition to Baluchistan. Some time was to elapse before I first met her, and I owe an immense debt of gratitude to her for her encouragement, which started with that first letter. Secondly I received an extraordinarily kind and encouraging letter from Piggott himself, of which the gist was, in effect, that my arguments deserved to reach a wider audience through publication. I then set down my ideas but nothing happened until a young American archaeologist, Dr Robert H. Dyson Jr, saw my manuscript by accident and suggested writing some authoritative archaeology into it. The combined effort was eventually published in our joint names in the *American Anthropologist* in 1961.

About the same time another accident—the chance discovery of a pair of ancient mounds some fifty miles south of Quetta—introduced me to the excitement of field archaeology. The mounds at Isplinji were urgently reported to the Pakistan Archaeology Department because, in a rain gully in one of the mounds, a complete skeleton and several remains of others, with what appeared to be grave goods, had been exposed. An almost complete skull was recovered intact. It was extremely brittle and delicate and had to be protected with wax (several pounds of candles, my best saucepan and an operation that resembled icing a cake). The most important consequence, however, was a visit to Isplinji with Mr Harunur Rashid, archaeologist, and Mr Sadardin, excavation foreman, from the department. They showed me what to look for on the surface of the mounds, and later Raoul Curiel, the Director of the Archaeological Department, encouraged me to watch for other places of interest on my travels. The next few months were very rewarding and revealed quite a number of new sites, some of which Beatrice de Cardi was able to visit later at my suggestion. Among the sites of major interest that I found at this time were the Harappan town of Judeir jo daro north of Jacobabad, and Pirak near Sibi where there is a plentiful ceramic of unique designs and, so far, unknown origins and connections. Publication of the Pirak material in two articles was my first incursion into archaeology as such.

I do not remember when I first read O. G. S. Crawford's *Archaeology in the Field.* Apart from being a masterpiece of enormous interest to professional and layman alike, its insistence on the importance of surface exploration was an inspiration to me. It would be tedious to trace, even if I could remember them, the steps by which I gradually became more deeply involved, but the publication of a tentative hypothesis of the causes of the decline of the Indus Civilisation in the *American Anthropologist* almost certainly converted what had until then been amicable exchanges of ideas with Dr George F. Dales of the University Museum in Philadelphia into an even more amicable professional collaboration. This led to further collaboration with the University Museum and Fondazione Lerici at Sybaris, and with Diana Kirkbride (now Mrs Helbaek) and Hans Helbaek at Beidha. Since then archaeology has occasionally threatened to take over all the time I could spare from building up a practice in my own profession, but if sometimes it has encroached on this it has amply repaid the debt by providing a new time dimension in modern hydrological studies.

What started as mainly destructive criticism of the deductions of archaeologists in the field of environment, happily became constructive as soon as I was jointly involved with archaeologists. I am still highly critical, as will appear later, of uninformed pronouncements on water and weather in their relationship to prehistory, but the basic objective of this book is to offer a constructive approach to environmental problems from a new direction.

The introduction of any new approach to archaeological problems must involve a difficult choice. To whom should it be introduced? Should it be aimed mainly at archaeologists? At other specialists whose work contributes to the solution of archaeological problems? Or at those who have a wide but unspecialised interest in the past?

I have tried to write for all these rather different interests and the choice has seemed to me inevitable because most archaeologists and specialists are laymen where this new approach is concerned. They are mostly no better and no worse equipped than the third group, the intelligent amateurs of archaeology, for understanding of the technicalities involved. This therefore is not intended as a text book even for those whose speciality is intimately concerned with water and weather. I have assumed a common interest in archaeology and the probability that only a few readers will really know anything about water and weather, or have applied this knowledge to archaeology, so I have devoted much space to describing as simply as I can what hydrology is all about and how it links up with almost every aspect of environment studies. Not all the description is directly relevant to archaeology, but unless I can convince people firstly that the practical methods employed in hydrology are sound, and secondly that it touches almost every aspect of environment I cannot expect it to be taken seriously.

After statement of the basic principles, and of their relevance to other subjects such as geomorphology and ecology, the review of existing beliefs and of the evidence on which they are based can be undertaken rationally without laying oneself open to a charge of didacticism. This therefore follows immediately after the description of the technical background, and in its turn is followed by a very generalised attempt to put early man in an ecological framework.

In order to avoid giving the impression of working in realms of rarified theory I have devoted some space in Part III to some problems on which I have worked that have involved use of some of the basic principles.

I do not believe that any one scientific aid is intrinsically better or worse than others, or that there is a unique way to the truth: I am convinced that there is a case for truly interdisciplinary studies, of much wider scope than is usually considered necessary. Archaeologists are themselves highly specialised, too specialised sometimes to appreciate fully either the whole range of environmental factors involved or to know all the kinds of specialisation involved. It should therefore, I think, be regarded as a matter of course that specialists in certain fields—such as ecology, soils science, hydrology, and geology—should be consulted, just as it is now accepted without question that palynology and radiocarbon tests are essential. The consultation of a wide range of specialists by an archaeologist does not detract in any way from his authority, as he remains responsible for whatever interpretation may arise from interdisciplinary studies. The captain of a ship loses none of his responsibility merely because he has engineers, caterers, radar and radio specialists, and a doctor under his command.

PART I

THE ROLE OF WATER IN ENVIRONMENT

1 INTRODUCTION

To take anything for granted is, in a real sense, to neglect it and that is how most of us treat water.

It is a constant part of our background. As rain it nourishes our crops of all kinds and our ornamental gardens. Withdrawn from rivers or from wells it can be used for irrigation, to mitigate the vagaries of rainfall, or to support agriculture where this would otherwise be impossible. Plain or aerated, more or less diluted with alcohol, or disguised by infusions such as tea, it quenches thirst. Evaporated from our skins it cools us. It is no accident that the most discussed topic of conversation is, and probably always has been, the weather. For we talk of the weather largely in terms of the presence or absence of rain. In fact we, and all other living land organisms, animal and vegetable, have developed from watery ancestors and, if we cannot live by bread alone, we certainly cannot live at all without water.

The scientific study of water is known as hydrology. As it is a comparatively recent addition to the large range of applied sciences I shall describe its purposes, its methods, and its limitations in a later chapter. Its value in relation to problems of today is generally admitted, so that it is rare to find any major land-use development—in the widest sense of the term—undertaken without at least a preliminary hydrological appraisal. Obvious examples are schemes for irrigation, hydro-electric power, domestic water supply, storm drainage, and flood control. Less obvious, until one has had the experience of being stranded because of a washed-out line or road, is the need for hydrological investigations in the case of railways and roads. Beginning with the basic one of domestic water supply, these needs have developed in step with man's progress throughout history; and one of the objects of this book is to trace the intimate connection between man's social and technical development and his increasing control of water.

Hydrology will be described here as simply as possible, but in some detail because it deals with certain fundamental rules of behaviour of water that affect, in one way or another, almost every aspect of physical environment. These rules depend ultimately on the physical and chemical properties of water and are the same for all parts of the earth's surface and have been the same at all periods of the earth's history. I was tempted at one stage to call this book Palaeohydrology, but thought better of it. The immediate reason for rejecting the name was that the prefix *palaeo*, in so far as it has any generally accepted meaning, tends to belong to the palaeolithic period, with which this book is not concerned. A far more convincing reason is that there was nothing inherently different in the behaviour of water simply because it was prehistoric. The climate of any particular place almost certainly differed at times in the past from the climate of today, but precipitation of all kinds, streamflow and evaporation followed exactly the same laws then as now.

It is irrelevant that these laws and the whole complicated chain of cause and effect that govern hydrological phenomena may still not be completely understood. The same can be said of many sciences and of all those in which empiricism plays a part. What is relevant is that a given set of hydrological parameters, of which some, such as soil permeability, have been borrowed from sister sciences, would give the same results today as they would have given a million years ago. There is no prehistoric or *palaeo*-hydrology as such. To the extent, therefore, that the hydrological parameters of the past can be estimated with precision, the use of this discipline in archaeology can confer an objectivity lacking in some of the other archaeological tools.

The defintition of a parameter in the *Concise Oxford Dictionary* is a 'quantity constant in the case considered, but varying in different cases'. Examples are temperature, rainfall, the rate at which water can infiltrate into a given soil and so on. Knowing the values to be ascribed to a number of such parameters in a certain situation, it is possible to calculate the value of some other dependent variable in the same situation. For example, a knowledge of temperature, relative humidity, solar radiation, and movement of the air as wind enables the potential evaporation to be calculated.

As hydrological relationships are timeless a knowledge of their nature can be used to deduce what the circumstances were at a remote time, provided that sufficient of the parameter values are known or can be assumed with reasonable accuracy.

Assuming for the moment that this proviso can be sufficiently often satisfied for hydrology to be accepted as an archaeological tool, a general exposition of the problem seems to be the next step. This can best be done in the form of a number of statements of which the truth is fairly self-evident in each case.

1. Climate is an inescapable and essential part of human, animal, and vegetational environment. This does not require any elaboration beyond pointing out those climatic phenomena that are most relevant. They are: rainfall and its type and seasonal incidence; temperature and its range and particularly the duration of frost; humidity and evaporation; the annual variability of all these; and the incidence and duration of drought.

2. Any human settlement, in the absence of sophisticated means of relieving the stresses caused by climatic extremes, has perforce to be sited where such extremes are tolerable by man and by his sources of food, and where water is available for drinking.

3. As man developed techniques, some of which might well be called proto-engineering, for mitigating climatic stresses, he used structures of which the ruins sometimes survive. Examples are wells, river diversions, terracing and, later, underground galleries, storage cisterns, and dams. (This is not to overlook some very intelligent agricultural techniques of great antiquity, that were used sometimes alone but more often in conjunction with simple engineering.) The correct identification of such structures is essential to a full understanding of how primitive man lived, why he selected his village sites, and of his technical advance.

4. All through prehistory and history down to our times, both natural and man-induced disasters have had profound

effects on man's evolution. The further back in time one goes the more profound were the effects. Natural disasters have included floods, prolonged droughts, earthquakes, diseases, and such events as locust infestations. Generally slower in their effects, man-induced disasters have included deforestation leading to erosion, exhaustion of the soil, wars, over-grazing, over-population and destruction of animal sources of food. Nearly all these have at least a hydrological aspect: some are purely hydrological. When man, as a result of any of the above types of disaster, was forced to migrate, his ability to do so was entirely dependent on the existence, within easy reach, of other reasonably fertile and well-watered land or of migration routes along which at least water was available. Admittedly this did not pose much of a problem in temperate lands, but in the Middle East where civilisation started it was (and is to some extent still) a matter of great importance.

I have made four broad statements and all have this in common that they involve both water availability and man's ability to benefit from it. This common factor has not so far been studied in its own right. Often its importance is admitted but seldom has the study of it been entrusted to those whose business it is to know something about it. These are essentially hydrologists, ground-water geologists and those engineers whose interest lies in irrigation and water supply.

Much work has been done on prehistoric environment and, for the post-glacial period in particular (geologically known as the Holocene), those soil scientists, ecologists, palynologists, geomorphologists, and zoologists who have written about it have acknowledged indirectly the importance of water by the frequency with which they have interpreted the evidence in their own fields in terms of climate change. The few climatologists who have written of this period have generally been more cautious.

The Holocene is the period with which I am concerned, for two reasons. The first is that only for it is it possible to justify certain conclusions about the climate that provide the necessary premise for the use of known hydrological parameters. The second is that, on present evidence, the beginning of the Holocene is the earliest possible *terminus ab quo* for those conditions that led to the establishment of fixed human settlements based on agriculture. The conclusions will appear in due course: my concern with the period of human settlements is because these, by limiting mobility, set man in a more or less fixed environmental framework.

It might seem reasonable to suggest that a work such as this should be undertaken by climatologists, and indeed an authoritative full-length contribution from one of them, interested also in prehistory, would be of great value. It would not, however, be sufficient by itself: just as my conclusions will stand or fall according to the extent to which they fit the evidence of pollen analysis, palaeosols, and the rest, so would climatological conclusions have to fit the hydrological evidence.

Many people may find it hard to distinguish between the phenomena that I claim as being the proper study of the hydrologist and those that they consider to be the concern of the climatologist. So it is best to define the difference as I see it. Climatologists are concerned with the whole broad picture of movements of air masses and their interaction, with short-term and secular change, and with both extra-terrestrial and terrestrial causes of such changes. They are concerned with the basic atmospheric reasons for the extraordinary differences of rainfall between deserts on the one hand and humid tropics on the other, and, if they are interested in palaeoclimates, they are concerned with finding rational explanations for the climatic oscillations of the Pleistocene. Where rainfall is concerned they are more interested in broad classifications and hardly at all in the local meteorological circumstances that can make these broad classifications very misleading. Their most valuable contribution of all to the climatic background of water availability is their insistence that climate is a world-wide phenomenon.

Hydrologists rely on climatologists for the broad overall picture and on meteorologists for filling in the local details but, unlike these specialists who are mainly concerned with the conditions that can give rise to rain, gales, dry spells, and so on, they are concerned with the results. The climatologist is not concerned with rain as something that falls on the earth, supplies the needs of crops and animals, creates floods or is absorbed, whereas the hydrologist is mainly concerned with such matters. Clearly, therefore, both disciplines could usefully contribute to archaeological studies, but they should not be confused and the one should not be employed while the other is excluded.

Further, I am not trying to claim that the study of water in the prehistoric environment is more important than other environmental studies. It would be absurd to relegate to positions of lesser importance the effects of soils, climate, geology, vegetational associations, and of geographical factors such as altitude and latitude. But I do claim that most of these either depend to a considerable extent on hydrological factors or have, as in the case of altitude and latitude, a direct and predictable effect on the hydrological factors. And it follows that those who study these phenomena should have the best available hydrological advice to guide them.

Much more important, I am not arguing in favour of exclusive environmental determinism. While the floral part of prehistoric man's environment and consequently much of his faunal environment were largely determined by a complex of environmental factors, the argument cannot be extended to man himself. C. Daryll Forde put the problem in perspective. When he wrote in *Habitat, Economy and Society*, 'The study of the relations between cultural pattern and physical conditions is of the greatest importance for an understanding of human society but it cannot be undertaken in terms of simple geographical controls alleged to be identifiable on sight', he was writing in the context of existing cultures and economies that have survived at a lower, sometimes practically negligible, level of technical development. He illustrates the enormous diversity of cultural patterns that can exist, sometimes even side by side, in similar physical environments and recognises the complexity of a problem compounded of history (including cultural inertia) in all its aspects, economics, and environment. All determinisms, whether environmental, sociological, or economical, are warned against, and rightly, while the importance of each is recognised.

The other environmental sciences that are now being used increasingly by archaeologists are: botany (and its specialised aspects such as palynology or pollen analysis), zoology, soils (pedology), and geomorphology. In reaching tentative conclusions about climate, rainfall, floods, drainage, and other matters that concern me, I have had to make use of some evidence from all of these and I hope that in their turn specialists in these sciences will take the evidence of hydrology into account. We are all to a considerable extent interdependent and we are all looking for the truth in our various ways. If we really combine forces we shall find it much more easily.

My dependence on botanical evidence will appear later. If vegetation depends to some extent on hydrological factors, as surely everyone must agree that it does, a proper interpretation of vegetation must depend on a correct interpretation of hydrology. Similarly, soils cannot be considered either in isolation or against a generalised background of wetness or dryness. The formation of a particular type of soil is the result of the interaction of climate, drainage, geology, and vegetation. It does not, for instance, result merely from a hot climate with seasonal rainfall, but from a certain fairly definable range of mean annual rainfall having a certain seasonal distribution, and from the interaction of these and of temperature range.

When we come to geomorphology the situation is somewhat different, for by far the most active agent in geomorphological change is water, and the study of alluvial deposits and erosion without a good knowledge of hydrology should be unthinkable. For this reason two chapters are devoted entirely to geomorphology.

One of my several purposes is to remedy the present lack of precise thinking about the watery part of man's prehistoric environment. If I can persuade some archaeologists and others to limit their use of such descriptions as wetter, drier, warmer, more genial, to where each belongs—in casual conversation or in contexts where quantitative definition is unnecessary—I shall have achieved something. If I can persuade them that climate, in so far as it affects their studies, is really another way of describing available water, and that its vagaries can be estimated with a fair degree of precision, I shall have succeeded in opening the way to the infiltration—a particularly apt word in the circumstances—of some new ideas.

What do people mean when they write of wetter, drier, warmer, more genial, and all the rest of the comparative adjectives that are used so profusely? Wetter, drier, warmer and more genial than what? Generally than something whose characteristics are, to the user himself, equally unknown. And by how much? And was the difference really significant? And if so, in what way? These are not peevish or purely academic questions; their answers lie near the heart of many prehistoric problems.

The danger of the use of these expressions lies, as it does with all loose expressions, in the effect on the reader. The writer may, although I suspect that this is seldom the case, have some intuitive idea in his own mind about what he means, but the reader cannot share it. If he comes from an arid country he will equate geniality with lots of rain: if he comes from England he will probably equate it with unfailingly halcyon summer days or, if his tastes are different, with frost-free winter days and hounds running well on a good scent. The reader from an arid country would consider relative dryness disaster, while the mother of small children in England would think of it as a paradise in which the nappies dried quickly.

In the course of this book I shall inevitably challenge some cherished beliefs, not from any desire to debunk for the sake of doing so, but because it seems to me that a kind of cultural inertia besets the study of prehistoric environment. It is all too easy to ascribe uncritically to 'change of climate' happenings that had quite other causes, and all too easy to perpetuate views that seem obviously right but which, on examination, are very wrong. For instance, heavy alluviation is generally attributed to phases of high rainfall. In parenthesis, how high? In fact, alluviation is the end-product of erosion and depends on an erodible source of material and on conditions suitable both for erosion and for the transportation and deposition of eroded material. These conditions are the same and are not those of high rainfall.

An example of another type of cherished belief occurred in *The Times* on 13 August 1965, under the headline 'Neolithic

Finds at Sites in Cyclades'. The text contained the statement: 'Sheep were the principal animals kept and their presence in so great proportion suggests that the Cyclades then had a more moist climate, with better grazing than is available in their arid hills today'. One can only suppose that the writer had only met sheep in the Highlands of Scotland or in Wales. Anyone who has seen the sheep of Jebel Meidob in the Sudan, where the mean rainfall is about 150 mm. per annum, or those of Baluchistan, where the rainfall is very little more, will realise immediately the absurdity of this statement. None the less, the statement has been made and may already have acquired the authority of the printed word.

In later chapters I shall review the evidence for post-glacial climate change. As much of this evidence comes from specialised fields in which I am not qualified to question the deductions, I shall have to rely mainly on a common-sense objective review of some of the published data. When the deductions involve a hydrological conclusion I shall examine this in detail. Later I shall put forward alternative hypotheses that I believe will fit the general evidence just as well, and the hydrological evidence better, without postulating climate change. And so I hope at least to shake belief in those often quoted climate phases with their rather nordic-sounding names, the Boreal and all the rest; and in that elusive and timeless concept, the climatic optimum, with its misleading overtones of a sort of meteorological garden of Eden.

I do not seek to challenge the evidence for local and comparatively short-term changes in temperature and rainfall because it is irrelevant to my main argument. Making all due allowances for the natural human tendency to exaggerate and to make of a few isolated recorded instances of extreme cold or of exceptional wetness a 'little ice-age' or a century of abnormal cold, there is as much evidence for such short-term changes as there is against them. But, true or not, they are irrelevant because firstly there is no convincing evidence of such changes having been of sufficient amplitude to be ecologically significant, and secondly there is no evidence at all of the changes having been world-wide.

Looking back on one's own childhood and youth it is the exceptional years that are remembered most vividly. I remember the long, hot, dry summer of 1921, but I can picture much more vividly the isolated very cold winters of 1929 and 1946 because they made much more impact on me. In 1929 I was working as a plater's labourer in a frozen, draughty boiler shop on Merseyside, handling with inadequate leather mittens cold steel that removed the skin from my hands: nothing will ever eradicate the memory of the cold motor-cycle rides to work over frozen Wirral roads, or the sight of ice-floes in the Dee estuary. The memory of coal rationing and power cuts in 1946, with all outside work closed down for nearly two months, is nearly as vivid. If I had not been trained to regard such things objectively these traumatic experiences might have trapped me into claiming that there was a little ice-age of some twenty years duration about that time. Memories of mountain warfare training in Scotland during the same period would reinforce what would be a totally unfounded belief.

So, lest I be wrongly attacked at the outset for arguing that there has been no climate change at all in the Holocene—which I do not—let me admit immediately that probably, or at least possibly, there have been minor, short-term, local, and perhaps memorable, changes, but that these do not constitute climate changes as implied by the identification of the Boreal and Atlantic phases and all the rest.

To conclude this introduction of a new tool for archaeologists, I will try to fit it into the general picture as part of the already recognised need for an inter-disciplinary approach.

Archaeology is, or ideally should be, as varied as life itself, and requires for its pursuit nearly all the skills that are used in present-day environmental studies. In practice it and the archaeologists who profess it can often be divided into two main branches. One branch, with which this book is not very much concerned, is primarily interested in the search for and analysis of documents having a bearing on the political record. It is, therefore, in the nature of history as traditionally taught—1066 and all that. The other is more in line with the modern approach to history in that it is as much concerned with people as with personalities and events.

Social archaeology—there may be a better or generally accepted term for this—must, among other things, be a study in human ecology. This is the relationship between man as an individual, or as a social animal, and his physical environment. The rest of Social Archaeology is rightly concerned with human beings as thinkers, dreamers, worshippers of gods, devisers of laws and ethical codes, inventors, and artists; and with all those productive activities which are essentially economic in nature: in short all that distinguishes man from other social animals. The extent to which some of these subjects are themselves products of physical environment is outside the scope of this book. In Social Archaeology, wars, king lists, catastrophes are of use principally for providing dating milestones, the punctuations and sub-titles of the main story. Such events are of interest not as isolated episodes but as part of the whole causal chain.

Man's ecological environment comprises the soils, vegetation, fauna, climate, and topography in which he lives. For any particular habitat topography and latitude largely control climate, but the latter directly or indirectly controls all the other elements.

If the evidence of existing backward communities and of prehistoric cultures (which were communities) has been correctly interpreted, the form of human society has never been totally determined by the physical environment. But it is equally true to say that the part of man's environment that has provided him with food (the flora and fauna) has been very largely determined by the physical, inanimate environment. Generally speaking, the farther back one goes in time the more true this is. In more recent times man has himself increasingly affected his floral and faunal environment, but even as comparatively recently as the early Neolithic, man's only active means of mitigating his physical environment was the use of fire and of simple buildings in order to keep warm. His use of caves and of his mobility were passive reactions to environment. As soon as cultivation of crops and large-scale pastoralism were adopted by man, the existing symbiosis of flora and fauna was upset; this was man's first major influence on ecology.

So far I have only mentioned engineers in passing. Their rareness in prehistoric interdisciplinary studies in their own right is hard to understand. It may be due to lack of interest on their part or lack of opportunity. Their prehistoric prototypes were certainly at work very early in the history of human development. They may have been preceded by rainmakers and priests and, according to common but probably erroneous belief, by harlots: but they have a strong claim, as builders of terraces, stream diversions, and massive structures, to be classed among the earliest constructive professions. It seems, therefore, at least as reasonable to consult engineers as to consult architects. An engineer, faced with the almost vanished traces of a structure that was not a building, may mistake its original purpose, but he is less likely to do so than the average archaeologist who, through no fault of his own, might be hard put to it to distinguish between a dam and a barrage of today or between storm-water drains and soil sewers.

2 HYDROLOGY

Hydrology is a branch of applied science. It acts as a bridge, or should do, between the atmospheric physics of climatology and meteorology on the one hand and a whole range of activities of more obvious and direct interest on the other. This range includes botany, the scientific use of land for forestry, grazing, and agriculture, and those branches of engineering that promote the beneficial use of water or the control of its more unruly characteristics. The proper exercise of hydrology therefore necessitates a considerable understanding of both atmospheric physics and of ecology: and unless it is to be purely academic it requires a very considerable knowledge of engineering. Naturally, few if any hydrologists succeed in being the kind of polymath that this would imply, but the same is true today of almost every field, where the specialisation of the individual practitioner is in sharp contrast to the enormous scope of the discipline itself.

In attempting to describe hydrology to those for whom it is a new subject it is perhaps best to begin by summarising its origins. It is of mixed ancestry; it springs on the one hand from rain-makers and those who claimed to be able to foretell the weather; and on the other from dowsers and others who claimed to be able to find water underground. These and their descendants reigned unchallenged for thousands of years, until men like Francis Bacon began tentative speculation about periodic weather changes. Geographers were among the first to detect a hydrological factor in the shaping of the earth, but until very recently they did not go beyond general statements; eventually, however, they were to furnish one of the main streams of thought that contributed to the creation of scientific hydrology. In the meantime engineers began to feel the need for some reliable and calculable basis for the design of structures that had to do with the use and control of water and out of this need was born a second main stream of thought. The third stream was provided simultaneously by a specialised branch of geology interested in the extraction of water from underground. In the meantime, meteorology and climatology were making parallel advances.

It is only very recently that there has been a convergence of these independent lines of development and a gradual realisation that hydrology cannot be divided into the waters above the earth, those that flow or stand on the earth, and the waters under the earth. For all these forms of water are parts of one integral, inter-related continuum which bears the rather jejune name of the hydrologic cycle. It is implicit in this concept, but all too seldom recognised explicitly, that water—rather like matter—can hardly, if at all, be created or destroyed. It can, however, change its state from vapour to liquid, to solid, and vice versa, and this it constantly does.

In any cycle it is permissible by definition to enter at any point. The simple cycle of the hen and the egg is an example. It is easier, perhaps, to enter the hydrological cycle at the apparently unvarying point represented by the oceans. In the oceans overwhelmingly, and to a much lesser extent in permanent ice-caps, inland seas, and lakes, the quantity of water is virtually static. The oceans not only cover about four-fifths of the earth's surface: they contain many hundreds of times the amount of water that occurs in all other visible sources combined—rivers, lakes, ice-caps, snow and glaciers. So they make an obvious point of departure for the cycle.

Water is evaporated from the oceans' enormous, open surfaces and from the tiny areas of lakes and rivers. It is also evaporated from moist soil and transpired by living organisms. Evaporation and transpiration occur wherever and whenever the air in contact with open water, soil, or living organisms is not saturated: that is to say, when the air does not already contain the maximum amount of water vapour that is consistent with its temperature (highly variable) and its pressure (very much less variable). Even in the humid tropics the air is seldom saturated except in the early morning, when its lower temperature requires less moisture to saturate it, or during periods of rain. Those who have experienced monsoon conditions in Colombo or Dar-es-Salaam may protest that the relative humidity at those times was 100 per cent (which is saturation), or nearly so, *and* that the temperature was 95°F.; they may not be very wrong, but they *are* wrong. Maximum humidity generally coincides with the minimum temperature of the day and so for instance the early morning may have a combination of 100 per cent relative humidity and a mere 75°F. temperature, while the afternoon at its hottest may register 85 per cent relative humidity and 92°F. Both combinations are of course uncomfortable, and personally I find that the early morning cooler one is the worse. I once experienced the almost unbearable combination of 120°F. and 65 per cent relative humidity, but although I spent much time in the particular small hell where this happened it fortunately proved a rare combination.

This digression is not irrelevant if it succeeds in showing that an evaporation potential exists almost everywhere, even if only for part of each day. Little if any evaporation potential would exist over the oceans if the air blowing across them followed a smooth path for, if this happened, the air in contact with the sea would very quickly become saturated so that no further evaporation could take place. In fact, for many reasons that need not concern us here, the air over the oceans moves turbulently and creates a continuous if varying evaporation opportunity and an unfailing source of atmospheric humidity. Thus there is a constant transfer of water from its liquid state in oceans, lakes, rivers, soil, and vegetation into the atmosphere. There, through local turbulence, through convection due to unequal heating or variation of temperature during the day, or through the overall atmospheric circulation pattern that brings into contact air masses of different origins, part of the water vapour may condense as clouds. In suitable conditions, particularly at the boundaries of air masses, rapid convectional rising and cooling of air containing an adequate supply of minute condensation nuclei can cause further condensation and the formation of hailstones, snow, or rain, most of which returns to the surface of the sea as rain. The necessary cooling can be caused in other ways than by convectional activity.

The air over the oceans, even when it has lost some of its moisture charge as rain, hail, or snow, remains relatively moist and becomes in the process relatively cool as it provides part of the heat required to vaporise water (its latent heat). When this moist air crosses land masses a variety of circumstances can cause it to lose its moisture as rain. Basically these circumstances are the same as over the oceans but there is one added factor—that of the physical lifting and cooling of the air by high land (orographic effect). If the precipitation is in the form of snow in a place at a high altitude, it may, in its solid form as ice crystals, accumulate for months, with only a certain loss by direct ice-evaporation—called sublimation. At the end of the winter season the remainder melts and then behaves in much the same way as precipitation which has fallen elsewhere as rain. Snowfall on ice-caps and permanent glaciers becomes ice and goes into a form of static storage analogous to ocean storage.

Rain and ice-melt on land can do one of four things: (1) they can be absorbed into the surface layers of soil and rock and, if the quantity is small, they will sooner or later be re-evaporated or transpired; (2) they can be absorbed up to the limit of the capacity of the surface while the surplus flows across the surface or along channels creating what is called run-off*; (3) they can arrive at such times and in such quantities that absorption by the surface is continually reinforced to the point where deep infiltration occurs; or (4) they can undergo almost any combination of these conditions.

It is clear from the evidence of rivers that, on a world-wide basis, a considerable and fairly constant proportion of precipitation creates run-off. A large part of the flow of perennial rivers, however, is due to infiltration and the subsequent re-emergence of the infiltrated water as river base-flow or springs. This is often known as indirect run-off. With relatively few exceptions direct and indirect run-off return to the sea which was the starting point. Icebergs are one means by which polar ice-cap storage is released back to the sea.

The hydrologic cycle can be considered, therefore, as consisting of three main elements in motion. First there is the enormous reservoir represented by the oceans and permanent

* In deciding between run-off, runoff and run off I have chosen the first form as it has the authority of the *Manual of British Water Engineering Practice*.

ice-caps; secondly there is the upward and translatory movement of water vapour into and with the atmosphere; thirdly there is the downward and translatory movement of precipitation and run-off. The long-term constancy of ocean level and of average ice-cap volume points to a constant global balance between the evaporation and atmospheric movement phase and the precipitation and run-off phase. Obviously much of the cycle is impossible to measure and hydrology, in so far as it tries to study the whole cycle, has to deduce a great deal from the rainfall—run-off phase and terrestrial evaporation. The measurement of such matters is therefore important, not merely in a local context but in order to understand the whole cycle.

From the practical point of view, the point of view of the government or individual requiring water for drinking or irrigation or power, it is essential to know as much as possible about the rainfall, run-off, evaporation, infiltration part of the cycle on land at the place where the water is required. Users of water need to know from where they can obtain it and at what cost. The usual sources of water are: underground water tapped by wells or bore-holes; river flow through either direct extraction or storage reservoirs; direct collection and storage of rain-water; condensation on impervious surfaces, as in the case of much of Gibraltar's water supply; and, recently, fresh water distilled from sea-water or saline ground-water. In the case of all these except the last the water is of meteoric or atmospheric origin, and the user must know the amount that he can safely rely on over an indefinite period of years. All meteoric sources of water are extremely variable, the most variable and fundamentally most important being precipitation. All other climatic parameters are subject, at the particular place under consideration, to seasonal, periodic, or random variations, but none to an extent comparable with that of precipitation.

River flow, ground-water, and lakes all derive from precipitation, and in varying degrees all reflect its extreme variability. On the whole, ground-water is the least variable, as most aquifers (geological formations containing water) have sufficient storage capacity to even out the extreme variations. For instance, in large aquifers not subjected to pumping, the level of the water, or its pressure in the case of a confined aquifer, responds so slowly and so slightly to rainfall variations that only very precise measurements can detect change. A confined aquifer is one in which the water is under some degree of pressure owing to the existence of a relatively impermeable layer overlying it: such an aquifer gives rise to artesian or sub-artesian conditions if a means of escape is provided by drilling through the impermeable layer. However, even aquifers do respond to rainfall changes and it becomes essential to know the way in which the aquifer is recharged, by precipitation or seepage from rivers and lakes, themselves dependent on precipitation, if use of the water is contemplated. We attempt in the case of river flows to eliminate some of their inherent variability by constructing storage reservoirs that perform a function analogous to that of underground storage. Before undertaking a project to store water it is essential to know the flow régime of the river under varying conditions of precipitation.

Whether hydrological studies are undertaken for academic reasons or as a preliminary to projects for the use of water the problem is essentially the same—the analysis and interpretation of whatever data exist in order to try to establish reliable and rational relationships between different hydrological phenomena. Examples of such relationships are that of rainfall and run-off; of rainfall, run-off, infiltration, and evaporation; or of temperature, relative humidity, and evaporation. Some of these relationships depend on physical and topographic conditions, peculiar to the place studied, that may invalidate their application elsewhere unless the conditions are really the same. Most problems are so complex that any truly rational solution of them would involve a degree of detailed knowledge that is seldom economically obtainable. As examples one can quote relationships involving infiltration where types of surface soil, vegetation, slopes, land forms, and so on can vary enormously even within the area of a small catchment. In such cases it can be very misleading to apply relationships established under one set of physical conditions, perhaps even those of one part of a catchment area, to another area or other parts of the same catchment.

So, approximations have to be made very frequently and these require a great deal of experience and even some degree of intuition. The accuracy of these approximations can generally be checked by adhering strictly to the basic water balance formula. This states in the case of any area under study that: water entering the area minus evaporation minus infiltration equals change of storage of surface water (including that held in the surface soil) plus water leaving the area.

The changes of storage can be either positive or negative; and sometimes it is possible to substitute for infiltration the change in underground storage. In the case of a whole river catchment, water entering the area is precipitation plus the discharge of any springs that, on geological grounds, must receive their recharge from outside the area: both are measurable.

Methods exist for the direct measurement of evaporation from open water surfaces and for the calculation of evapotranspiration from temperature, humidity, and solar radiation data as well as from those direct measurements which apply only to open water surfaces. With care, experience, and skill this factor in the water balance can be calculated with acceptable accuracy. Change of storage involves measurements of soil moisture at representative points and the recording of changes of level of lakes, ponds, and other forms of surface storage: therefore it too is susceptible of reasonably accurate measurement, though this is all too rarely undertaken in the case of soil moisture. Water leaving the area is fairly easily measured provided that a gauging site on the river is available at the outlet of the area studied, where the bed materials and shape are stable and the velocity of flow not too great. This leaves infiltration, or change in ground-water storage, which is by far the most difficult. Obviously, however, if all the other factors are known what is left must be infiltration. Geophysical methods used in conjunction with observation wells provide a useful check on the estimate of infiltration but cannot, for obvious reasons, reach a high degree of accuracy unless observation wells are uneconomically numerous.

The problem is naturally far more complicated than this outline suggests, and to appreciate this point, one has only to consider the fact that usually all the components of the equation are continually changing. In certain circumstances, however, particularly in arid and semi-arid areas where all the components are episodic, it is possible to develop what is in effect a series of simultaneous equations by observing a large enough number of episodes.

What is the relevance of all this to archaeology? The purpose of this book is to show that it *is* relevant, even if mainly indirectly. For studies of this kind establish recognisable patterns connecting the type of precipitation, the topography on which it falls, the state of vegetation or denudation, and the resulting ground-water level and run-off. The relevance is greater precisely where the method is easiest to apply, in arid and semi-arid areas; and such areas contain almost all the relics of early prehistoric settlements that have survived in the Middle East. It depends partly on the fact that rivers in such areas are almost always characterised by flash floods whose magnitude in the past can be gauged from the dimensions and slope (generally known as the geometry) of their beds and flood-plains. In the case of many prehistoric settlements, evidence exists in the form of ancient well shafts of where the water table stood when the settlements were occupied.

In arid and semi-arid areas, which are, generally speaking, those with strictly seasonal rainfall and mean annual totals of rainfall of not more than 250 mm. and 500 mm. respectively, the effect of vegetation on run-off is not very marked for reasons that will be explained later when water is considered as an ecological factor. The effect of vegetation on infiltration should on the face of things be appreciable, but there are certain self-compensating factors that tend to minimise the effect in practice.

If, therefore, the climate of the prehistoric period in question can be estimated in terms of rainfall, it becomes possible to assess the whole pattern of run-off and ground-water in terms of phenomena that one can measure or estimate from the data of today.

In most areas of archaeological interest some hydrological data exist, and where this is not so one can make fairly close estimates of them by comparing geological, vegetational, and geomorphological indicators with those in other areas where the rainfall and other elements of environment are known. Unfortunately, data tend to be scarce and of uncertain quality, as anyone knows who has tried to build up a coherent picture from them. In any place or country with considerable annual or seasonal variations of precipitation, temperature, and other factors, these variations can completely hide inaccuracies. For at first glance a time series of several years of precipitation records will look much the same if the years of low precipitation are genuine as it would if the low figures are due to the fallibility of the observer.

As the results of a hydrological study can be no more accurate than the data on which they depend, it is relevant to the use of such a study in archaeology to give a brief description of how data are collected, how errors occur, and how they can be identified and corrected. All forms of hydrological and climatological data have some contribution to make to an understanding of the whole physical environment, but in the case of archaeological problems certain factors such as rainfall and stream flow are of greater importance than temperature and humidity that exhibit far less variation from one year to another. These more significant aspects will therefore now be described in greater detail than the others.

Precipitation, as the ultimate source of practically all the water used by man and his environment, is clearly the most important of all. It would not be an exaggeration to say that if the rainfall of a country is known in great detail most of the rest of the hydrologic cycle can be inferred from it and the geographical location. Fortunately precipitation is much easier to measure with reasonable accuracy than any other hydrological parameter and, perhaps as a direct result of this, precipitation records almost everywhere are geographically more numerous and are of longer duration than any others except perhaps those of temperature. Some records extend back in time for as much as 200 years.

The description given here applies only to rainfall, for accurate measurements of snowfall and dew are of recent introduction and a satisfactory method of measuring hail has not, so far as I know, been evolved. Rainfall depths are measured by rain-gauges of more or less standard design and operation, though it must be emphasised that the adoption of standards is fairly recent so that old records may contain built-in errors due to faulty exposure or design. Essentially a rain-gauge consists of a funnel of a certain diameter to collect or catch rain and lead it to a container. The rim is normally machined with a sharp edge having an inside diameter of exactly five inches, but occasionally it may be larger. The rain collected in the container is measured twice a day by pouring it into a graduated glass cylinder calibrated to read the catch of rain directly as hundredths of an inch (cents) or millimetres. If hail falls the chances are that some will bounce out of the funnel.

The main sources of error are human. Apart from negligence on the part of the observer, which can be a major and entirely unpredictable factor as can excess of misplaced zeal, errors arise out of faulty exposure of the gauge and faulty readings. Exposure is faulty if, for instance, the site is screened even partially by buildings or trees; if the site is exposed to high winds; and if the level of the rim above ground is so low as to allow the catch to include raindrops bounced or splashed off the ground or so high that wind effects become considerable. Nowadays certain simple rules are laid down and if these are observed, errors due to faulty exposure are small. When it comes to measuring the catch, the human element can be considerable as laboratory conditions are not practicable for thousands of scattered rain-gauges. The observer may obtain a false reading by failing to hold the calibrated measuring glass truly vertical, or he may make a mistake in judging the level of the water between adjacent graduations: if there has been sufficient rain to fill the gauge glass several times he may forget how many times he has filled it and fail to preserve the catch in another container so as to make a second measurement as a check. Gauge glasses are fairly easily broken and their immediate replacement is sometimes difficult in remote places, and then the observer may guess the depth or just not bother to measure it at all.

Exposure errors tend to be systematic; that is, they give constantly low records (hardly ever too high). If their existence is suspected, they can be rectified either by putting a new gauge correctly exposed near the old one and observing the two together for several years or, where this is not practicable, by using statistical techniques for relating the old record to the new one after re-siting the original gauge. Observer errors tend to be random but with a slight bias towards low results in the case of great depths of rainfall. Random errors generally have little overall effect.

Unfortunately gross negligence on the part of the observer can and does occur. The observer becomes ill or goes on holiday without making arrangements for a substitute, or he entrusts the readings to someone else who does not understand what is required. I know of a case of two fairly closely adjacent gauges, one at a secondary school and the other at a primary school. In each case the schoolmaster was the observer. When the records were compared and checked by statistical methods, that at the secondary school was found to be worthless while the other was good. Probably the secondary school teacher had been getting a succession of pupils to note the readings for him. But rain-gauges at schools, often the only place in a remote area where it is possible to find a literate observer, are notoriously susceptible to childish pranks and one often wonders to what extent unusual records of great depths of rain have been due in part to children supplementing the rainfall. It should be one of the factors taken into account in fixing a standard height for the rain-gauge rim.

Errors can arise from sheer well-meaning stupidity. Tales of this kind are legion but I can personally vouch for two classic examples in which the observer, proud of his gleaming new instrument, protected it from the rain. In one case he took it into his tent whenever the sky looked threatening: in the other he built a little thatched roof over it to save the trouble of moving it. In another case the observer, and his supervisor, had failed to see the implications of a seedling mango tree a few yards from the rain-gauge. By the time I saw it the gauge was almost as effectively protected from rain as the one that had a thatched roof.

Sometimes zeal can have a positive result. In a certain very remote mountain valley three of the four tiny villages had rain-gauges. The head man of the fourth village, seeing them as status symbols, insisted on having one too: he was a man of determination carrying an assortment of lethal hardware and backed by a band of men similarly determined and equipped. His assurance that one man in the village could read and write was not, in the circumstances, questioned and the rain-gauge was installed. The records came in punctually, legible and superficially consistent with those of neighbouring gauges. When the field supervisor made a routine spot check some months later he asked the observer to go through the motions of measuring water that he poured into the gauge. After an embarrassed silence the observer admitted that he could neither read nor write. The explanation was quite unexpected. Twice a day, morning and afternoon, the observer decanted the catch of rain, when there was any, into the measuring cylinder which he corked securely; and twice a day he mounted his donkey and rode, clutching the gauge glass and his pad of record forms, to the nearest literate observer some five miles away. His friend read the gauge glass and filled in the form and the observer returned to his village with, presumably, the feeling of a job well done. Unfortunately this kind of devotion to duty is rare.

It must now be fairly obvious that there is a virtual certainty of random error, which does not matter; a considerable chance of systematic error that can be eliminated by appropriate analytical methods; and an unknown degree of crazy errors or of those due to negligence, also susceptible of detection by using the right methods. It must be equally obvious that crude, that is unchecked, rainfall data is often worthless. It follows, therefore, that all data must be checked by those who know the methods involved: it is not a job for an amateur unless he has mastered these methods, which are not particularly difficult. Checking can be done in various ways. By one method the records of each gauge in a group are compared with those of the group as a whole. If the data are very numerous, the whole process can be done by computers. When the whole group has a continuous record of a sufficient number of years, the results reveal those years, seasons, months, or even days (depending on the basis of analysis) for which the record is inconsistent. It can also reveal the point in time at which the record of a particular gauge, after being reasonably consistent at one level of rainfall, suddenly becomes consistent at another level. Where this has occurred the record either before or after the change has obviously been subject to systematic error, and often a search of the records will show that the exposure of the gauge was changed at that time. It is not always necessary to reject incomplete records or those in which isolated or systematic errors are found. Provided that some gauges in the group, preferably not less than ten or so, have complete and consistent records, gaps in the records of other gauges or isolated errors can be made good by establishing correlations between those other gauges and the group. Sometimes it is permissible to include in the group stations where a systematic error has been verified and corrected.

It is absolutely essential that the records checked in this way should be all from a hydrologically homogeneous area, which generally means also a fairly small area.

Sometimes the essential requirements of a long period of record or of a reasonably dense network of gauges, or both, are lacking. When this happens much depends on the experience and ability of the hydrologist, and it is more than ever essential that the analysis of whatever records there are should not be left to an amateur.

So far I have only dealt with one form of rainfall information, that of its daily depth, from which can be deduced the mean rainfall, its mode of variation over periods of years, and its seasonal and monthly distribution. Daily records of themselves give no information about the type of rain, its intensity and how long the storm lasts, and how the intensity varies during the storm. Although the importance of intensity and duration have long been recognised, it is only recently that sufficient numbers of automatic recording gauges have been installed, even in advanced countries, for reliable information to be obtained. For a very long time intensities were inferred from daily or half-daily totals of rain. This is not even very valid in countries where wide-spread continuous rain is common; in the case of countries having sporadic high intensity storms it is meaningless.

Analysis of the charts of automatic recording rain-gauges gives a very clear idea of the rainfall factor in run-off and infiltration problems, and indeed these cannot be solved satisfactorily without intensity information. Study of these characteristics of rainfall are not dependent on many years of record for there is no evidence whatever to connect the incidence of high intensity storms with high annual or seasonal totals—except that in a year or season of high rainfall there is a greater chance that a particular combination of intensity and duration will occur. Lack of a long-period record can thus be partly compensated for by a dense network of recording gauges. By making an assumption that has not yet been proved but appears logical—that any particular combination of intensity and duration would, if the record were of many years, have a certain frequency of occurrence related to the mean annual rainfall—it is possible to use the short-term records of many gauges in a particular locality to establish these frequencies. The importance of this will appear when the connection between rainfall intensity and the amount of run-off and infiltration is considered.

The other principal types of hydrological observations are those concerning stream-flow, ground-water levels, temperature, solar radiation, relative humidity, evaporation pan readings, soil temperature, the directions and velocities of wind, and the variations of all these. They are of vital importance to evaporation and transpiration studies and are therefore of direct use to agriculturists as well as engineers. I shall not describe them here because this is not intended as a technical treatise. The description of rainfall measurements is more than enough to show that hydrological data collection must be undertaken with care and understanding by people who are trained in its techniques.

A full description of interpretative methods would also be out of place, but an outline of the problem is necessary to an understanding, however partial, of the place of water in the environment.

When rain reaches the earth's surface at a certain intensity, measured in millimetres or inches per hour, what happens to it? If the surface is thickly covered by vegetation a certain amount of the rain is intercepted by and retained on leaves, twigs and so on; it is not retained permanently on them but will not begin to flow off them until a certain 'wetness' is achieved, and this same wetness will still be there at the moment when the rain ceases. Interception and retention therefore have the double effect of delaying the moment when the rain reaches the soil and of absorbing a small amount that never reaches the soil. The effect can be considerable in dense forest but may be largely ignored in semi-arid or arid conditions. Dense forests are rarely the setting for early prehistoric farming settlements so need no further consideration here.

Semi-arid vegetation, once it has become well established towards the end of the season of rainfall, intercepts very little rain but has some local effect in reducing the energy of impact of raindrops. Before it becomes seasonally established it has virtually no such effect. Assuming that the raindrops strike the earth with little if any loss of energy, their fate depends on the type of surface that they strike and its ability to absorb water. If the surface is composed of a well-graded soil, containing a certain proportion of clay particles but otherwise fairly permeable owing to normal weathering and the action of roots and soil fauna, high energy raindrops have the rather unexpected result of creating a thin, relatively impermeable skin through 'puddling' action. As a result water, unable to penetrate the surface appreciably, moves across it as run-off. The run-off carries with it some of the puddled clay in suspension, so that if the rainfall is of long duration infiltration gradually increases. With considerable run-off the velocity of flow increases so that coarser particles are carried as well as the suspended clay. It is this sediment that gives flood-water its characteristic colour and turbidity, and what is happening is a form of soil erosion.

If the rain falls on a highly permeable gravel surface, only the difference between the rainfall intensity and the infiltration rate will run off. Sometimes in such cases very high intensity is required before run-off can occur. Much the same applies to sand surfaces, but these generally contain some proportion of very fine particles so that the effects are intermediate between those of normal soils and gravel.

Bare rock can produce surprising results. Nearly all bare rock surfaces are fissured and fractured to a quite considerable depth by weathering action, and in addition many are stratified into beds with more or less permeable joints and with similar transverse joints. When rain falls, the surface fissures and fractures fill to capacity fairly quickly and may absorb the greater part of a brief rainstorm. What is left over runs off to an extent depending on the difference of rainfall intensity and the rate of infiltration into beds and joints; the matter does not rest there, however, for the run-off may cross zones of highly permeable beds and joints. On some limestone and sandstone formations the absorption and infiltration of rain is very high indeed, and the same can apply to basalts when these show vertical columnar fracture in shallow thicknesses.

When vegetation is well established its main effect is to reduce somewhat the velocity of overland run-off as well as the puddling effect of raindrops. It is partly in this way that vegetation reduces soil losses by erosion, and partly by the binding effect of roots. All the illustrations given assume implicitly that the earth's surface is dry at the beginning of rain. If it is already soaked from a previous storm the sequence of events is modified.

Run-off and infiltration are certainly very complicated matters to understand for those not familiar with them. In my description of these operations up to the moment when run-off begins, I have attempted to concentrate on the common sense that underlies them.

This description of practical hydrology opened with the gathering of facts about rainfall. It then traced the various ways in which the rainfall in excess of that which is intercepted, absorbed, or infiltrated begins to flow over the surface of the land. To complete the surface water balance I must now follow up what happens to run-off and infiltration and show how they create base-flow and floods. Finally we shall emerge again into the realm of measurable facts at the point where both these kinds of flow are measured at the outlet of an area of study.

Overland flow moves at velocities and depths that depend on the slope and roughness of the land and on the quantity that is flowing.

On any element of the earth's surface the run-off is composed of two parts: one part derives directly from the rain falling on that element; the other is the result of rain that has fallen uphill from the element rather earlier. After a time which, other things being equal, depends on how long it takes for run-off from the element farthest uphill (which is by definition derived entirely from rain falling on it) to reach the downstream element we are considering, a steady state is reached with incoming rain plus run-off equalling outgoing run-off. For any particular intensity of rainfall, the resulting steady discharge will be reached when the duration of rainfall equals the time taken for run-off from the element farthest upstream to reach the outlet. If the rain continues at the same intensity, run-off will continue past the outlet but without any further increase of the rate of discharge. The higher the intensity the greater the rate of discharge. If continuous measurements are made of the rate of discharge at the outlet and plotted as a graph against time, the result is what is known as a *flow hydrograph*. In practice the situation is very much more complicated: rain seldom falls at a steady intensity; elements of the earth's surface, even within quite small areas, have very different run-off characteristics, the shape of the surface is highly irregular and rain may fall on only one small part of an area or on several widely separated small parts—to name but a few of the complications. But the reasoning is based fundamentally on the simple example described, in which infiltration has been ignored.

As run-off develops from its initial stage of a sort of shallow sheet flow, irregularities in the earth's surface, themselves often the result of earlier run-off, channel the flow along gulleys, depressions, and ultimately valleys. As the flow concentrates, its depth and velocity increase unless a flattening of the slope has a modifying effect. New tiny gulleys can form anywhere where a chance combination of factors results in locally deeper and swifter flow and consequent erosion.

Ultimately the combined elements of run-off from a storm or system of storms converge into a river. Once they have done this, whether the river is perennial or merely a torrent, they emerge from the undisciplined complications of local run-off into something that can be measured once again with precision. Many of those concerned with the estimation of floods and their frequencies prefer not to risk the uncertainties and difficulties of determining what happens between the origin of a flood as a storm and its verification as a flood. They prefer to base their estimates on analyses of flood records and, provided that records are numerous, this is an adequate way of determining the mean annual discharge of a river. But it cannot be relied on to give a reliable answer when the problem is to estimate either the mode of variation of annual discharge or the peak rate of discharge and total yield of exceptional floods. Even where rivers have been gauged for a great number of years, statistical frequency analysis of the results should not be relied upon unless the results are reasonably consistent with a more rational approach. The statistical concept of the flood which occurs once in so many years for a particular catchment area has its uses, but it must be fully understood and its limitations recognised. When adopted by amateurs it can be at best misleading and at worst dangerous.

Another concept which is of only very limited validity is that of the run-off coefficient. A moment's thought about the mechanics of run-off will show that even if rainfall intensity were the only variable, the percentage of rain that runs off must vary enormously from one storm to another. In practice, therefore, it is only legitimate to speak of a run-off coefficient in two contexts. The first is that of the individual storm and its resultant flood; the second is the long-term relationship, over a period of many years, between total rainfall and total discharge. In most perennial rivers and, to a very small extent only in some seasonal torrents, the total discharge is composed in varying degree of purely surface run-off and of what is sometimes called indirect run-off. This is water that has infiltrated into various aquifers and subsequently rejoined the main surface stream either through distinct springs, often distant from the main stream, or through the banks and bed of the latter.

I have tried to describe briefly the whole series of observations, analyses, relationships, and interpretations involved in hydrological research, and hope later to show how this can serve archaeology by providing a rational basis for the interpretation of an important part of the evidence of ancient sites and their surroundings. Not every aspect of this applied science is relevant to prehistoric studies, but as they are all closely interwoven it is necessary to understand all the parts in order to understand the whole.

3 WATER AND CLIMATE AS AGENTS OF GEOMORPHOLOGY—I

Geomorphology means literally the study of the earth's shape. As this shape, or rather its irregularities (the minute amounts by which the earth's form departs from that of an oblate spheroid) and their distribution, depend fundamentally on the geological structure of the earth, obviously all the major features are the concern of geologists. By major features I mean the main land masses, mountain ranges, ocean deeps, and the like. Peaks and ocean deeps are only major in relation to the physical scale of our immediate surroundings: on a global scale they are almost insignificant. Starting at sea-level, one would have to travel downwards more than 2,000 times the height of Mt Everest to reach the centre of the earth. The major known and measured movements of the earth's crust that have occurred in recent times, such as that of the San Andreas fault in California, are even more insignificant, for the ratio of their vertical amount to the height of Mt Everest is even smaller than that of the height of Everest to the earth's radius. In other words, a really major vertical movement may be only a few millionths of the earth's radius. For one accustomed to thinking of structures of any kind as being subject to elastic bending, compression, tension, and shear, due to their own weight and to external and internal forces, it sometimes seems almost unbelievable that the earth's crust could be as stable as it seems to be. Rocks of various kinds that compose it, however brittle they may appear to be, are capable of yielding elastically. A masonry arch will deflect without fracture under even a safe load by an amount that, in proportion to its span, is much greater than the amplitude of major earth movements in proportion to the earth's diameter.

I have rather stressed this point of view because I believe that often insufficient weight is given to the effect of crustal movement as a continuing phenomenon. The effect of a violent crustal movement is immediately evident in the form of earthquake damage; but its effect on drainage patterns, although far slower and not immediately obvious, could sometimes be just as catastrophic.

While study of the earth's crust as a relatively rigid but none the less yielding structure belongs to geology, the study of its interaction with weathering agencies is geomorphology in the ordinarily accepted meaning of that word. Some geomorphologists are geologists who have specialised in the behaviour of the earth's outside surface: others are geographers who have specialised in land-forms. Most hydrologists feel that they have a special stake in the subject, for a very great deal of the shaping of the earth's surface is done through the agency of water.

Changes in the shape of the earth's surface that are not directly due to structural movements of the earth's crust can only come about through the movement of material from one place to another. The agencies involved are wind and water and, to a far smaller extent, volcanic activity. All movement of material by water is due to the earth's gravitation and is therefore downward. Temporary upward movement can occur through the action of wind, but deposition of windborne material occurs ultimately as a result of gravity. Along sea coasts tidal activity may cause some upward movement of sediments and these are often moved subsequently by wind action. The tendency, therefore, is for the earth to be gradually worn down to an over-all flatness, material from hills and mountains being moved gradually to the oceans and deposited in them. The earth's surface does not ever reach the flat state implicit in this tendency, for crustal movements of various kinds, including those caused by redistribution of the load on the earth's crust, re-create relief.

That major part of the movement of solid material that has water as its agency can only be understood fully if the behaviour of the agency is itself understood.

All this movement of material is essentially erosion on a global scale and requires a source of material, a means of transportation, and a destination. In all cases except wind transport and activity along sea shores the destination must obviously be at a lower level than the source, and the way in which water will move material is governed by this difference of level and by the various slopes of the land surfaces between source and destination, and of course by the amount of water.

The source of the transported material is of two main types. The primary source is the earth's solid crust; secondary sources consist of material previously moved from the earth's crust and redeposited elsewhere.

The first type starts as solid rock. Under the action of diurnal heat variation, frost, wind, rain, and the wedging action of ice and tree-roots the surface of the rock becomes fractured. The zone of weathering can sometimes be quite deep and permits chemical changes, through oxidisation, for example, and solution of some of the constituent minerals. The finer products of weathering are removed downwards by water or away by wind. Eventually the weathering proceeds to a stage at which run-off or landslides remove the larger pieces, and the rolling and bouncing of these produce more fine material by abrasion, and smaller pieces by further fracturing. In one or other or a combination of these ways the original rock becomes converted into boulders and soil.

The other source material is in a very general sense alluvial. It has already been moved from its place of origin and, much transformed during the mechanics of movement, has been deposited somewhere downhill where it may even have become a relatively stable formation. It is fundamentally more subject to erosion than parent rock material as it is already broken down into particles that can easily be transported by water. An exception to this is the case of alluvial material that has become cemented through the deposition of suitable salts by water. If cementation is effective this kind of material behaves essentially as sedimentary rock although it may be of very recent origin.

Vegetation probably has little effect on the rate of weathering of rock-surfaces, for the protection it affords against temperature changes is offset by the effects of root growth. On all other surfaces the type and density of vegetation have a great effect on water-borne erosion. As the vegetation depends primarily on rain, both the agent of erosion and the vegetational protection involve hydrologic factors.

This is no place for a detailed and technical discussion of the mechanics of water-borne sediments, so certain broad generalisations will have to suffice. Sediments behave in water in a way that is almost entirely dependent on their particle size. Certain clays go into colloidal suspension from which only the action of a coagulating agent will precipitate them. All other clays will remain in suspension for considerable periods but will eventually settle to the bottom under gravity alone; generally speaking, they remain suspended for as long as the velocity of the water is sufficient to keep them so, and this velocity varies according to the particle size and other factors. Next in order comes the range of particle sizes classified as silts. These are maintained in something resembling suspension only so long as the velocity of flow is fairly high and to some extent turbulent. It is difficult to give an estimate of the necessary velocity for this varies considerably according to the particle size and the degree of turbulence. At progressively higher velocities and greater turbulence fine sand, medium sand, coarse sand, and even fine gravel can behave as if temporarily suspended. All these materials are carried in and with the flowing water for as long as the velocity and turbulence are sufficient: it follows that they are only carried for the distance over which these conditions are satisfied. A reduction of velocity due to any cause will result in deposition of those components of the transported material for which the velocity is no longer sufficient.

Apart from what is carried temporarily suspended in the flowing water there are two other classes of water-borne sediment. One is known as bed-load and consists of more or less coarse material, sometimes covering a fairly wide spectrum of particle sizes, that rolls and bounces along the river bed. The other, sometimes also classed as bed-load, is more like an extreme form of solifluction: that is, the bodily movement in mass of a saturated sediment in a river bed.

There are several systems of classification of sediments according to particle size. A typical one, known as M.I.T. (Massachusetts Institute of Technology) system, gives the following limits of particle size for various types of sediment:

fine (colloidal)	clay	less than 0·0002 mm.
medium	clay	0·0002 to 0·0006 mm.
coarse	clay	0·0006 to 0·002 mm.
fine	silt	0·002 to 0·006 mm.
medium	silt	0·006 to 0·02 mm.
coarse	silt	0·02 to 0·06 mm.
fine	sand	0·06 to 0·2 mm.
medium	sand	0·2 to 0·6 mm.
coarse	sand	0·6 to 2·0 mm.
	gravels etc.	over 2·0 mm.

The particle sizes that I have underlined represent the transition, according to this system, from clay to silt, silt to sand, and sand to gravel respectively. The particle size limits in any system are arbitrarily selected. In this particular system the largest particle size in each of the classifications is about three times the size of that of the next finer classification. Obviously, therefore, there is room for considerable variation in the behaviour of water-borne sediments even within one classification or 'fraction'.

In a naturally occurring soil, all or any of these classifications may be represented in almost any proportions. But when such a soil is totally carried by water each particle is free to behave in its own way and this is why sediments deposited from water show a stratified structure. In soil mechanics, the whole study of the behaviour of soil, the way in which various fractions are combined in various proportions, is the most important thing. In considering water-borne sediments the actual particle sizes are what matter. The characteristic laminated structure of water-deposited sediments affords a quick means of identifying the flow conditions that obtained before and during their deposition. If particle size analyses of the sediments from different laminations are made, this quick means can also become an accurate one.

It is not always necessary, however, to carry out analyses; a material containing more than a very small amount of clay can be identified as being clayey by simple field tests. If these tests are applied to a sample of an alluvial deposit and show that it is clayey, it follows that the sediment was deposited under still or almost still water. It does not matter that the clay may be mixed with various amounts of silt or even fine sand. At the moment when the clay was deposited the water was for all practical purposes stationary: that being so, all other coarser materials would automatically be deposited as well. If the structure is finely laminated with alternating very thin beds of sand, silt, and clay (generally in that order), one can assume that it is the result of frequent shallow flooding by sediment-laden water. If the deposit is weakly laminated, of great thickness, and consists of a reasonably homogeneous mixture of clay and silt, it can safely be deduced that it was laid down under sustained still water conditions such as those in a lake.

I have already defined the movement of material that changes the face of the earth as requiring a source, a means of transport, and a destination. In describing sediments I have unavoidably elided the last two requirements, and have thus shown that the kind and quantity of material transported, as well as the mode and location of its subsequent deposition, are directly related to water. In the chapters devoted to the relationships between hydrology and ecology I shall give examples of the extraordinary variability of rainfall. For the moment let it suffice that it is extremely variable both in annual amounts and seasonal distribution, and as between one storm and another. The brief description of run-off given earlier will have indicated why the floods that result from rain are even more variable.

The flood history of any river, and particularly of one liable to the kind of flood that will carry large amounts of sediment, is a story of many entirely different events. This is particularly so when the river only flows intermittently. A large perennial river can also carry sediments, but its perennial flow sets a lower limit to the possibilities of sediment deposition. In a river subject to intermittent flashy floods the amount of sediment will vary enormously between one flood and another and so will the source of material. Intermittent floods in normally dry rivers are frequently due to isolated intense storms that only affect a part of a catchment and only cause flow in parts of the drainage system. Material may therefore be brought down sometimes from hill situations, sometimes from valleys; and from widely differing soil and rock conditions.

The way in which any flood varies in its depth (or stage) and discharge as it passes a given point in a river can be shown graphically by plotting against time the instantaneous values of stage and discharge that were measured or calculated for particular moments of time. The use of suitable continuously recording equipment enables the curve of stage against time to be drawn directly. The corresponding curve of discharge against time is calculated from it. The results are known as the *stage hydrograph* and *discharge hydrograph* respectively for the particular place and flood.

No two hydrographs for a single gauging point are ever the same, except by pure coincidence: it follows that the capacity of floods to transport sediments is never the same. Part of a flood in a tributary stream may be sufficient to carry a high proportion of sediments in relation to the bed in which it flows and the slope. If, when it reaches the main river, it is not adequately reinforced by other tributary flows, it may become a quite insignificant flood in relation to the main river bed and slope. Having successfully carried sediments in the tributary bed it may suffer such a reduction of velocity in the main river that most of the sediment is dropped.

Many steep rivers with beds of sand, gravel, or boulders, normally dry and subject only to occasional floods, lose a great deal of their discharge by infiltration into the bed material. I know of a small river in Baluchistan subject to fairly frequent floods in its upper reaches that may occasionally attain discharges of as much as 300 cubic metres per second. Most of the upper-reach flood peaks, however, do not exceed about 30 cubic metres per second, and all those with this rate of discharge or less are totally absorbed by infiltration within about 50 kilometres. In Saudi Arabia, in a certain wadi there are on an average some ten floods a year at one point, of which only about one-fiftieth reach a point 30 to 40 kilometres downstream. In both these cases water enters the river bed alluvium and thereafter flows out of sight as sub-surface flow. The progressive reduction of surface flows means that the capacity of these to transport sediments is progressively reduced. Material brought down from mountain sides or moved along the river bed at the height of surface discharge is soon redeposited. The greater the areal extent of river-bed alluvium or valley-fill, the greater the rate at which a flood discharge is reduced by infiltration. As the level of alluvium builds up, the area increases. If rainfall and the floods that it causes follow for a long time a certain general pattern favourable to the deposition of sediments, a change in the general régime of sedimentation can only result from changes in the slope of the valley. These can be caused by tectonic or epierogenic movement of that part of the earth's crust over which the river flows; or they can be the result of sedimentation itself. This last is largely self-adjusting, for sedimentation in the upper reaches steepens the gradient and increases the velocity of flow so that water-borne material is deposited farther downstream.

In fact, the process of building up in the absence of movement of the earth's crust is self-generating so long as the rainfall and run-off conditions remain favourable for sediment transportation. It is often overlooked that freshly deposited uncemented alluvium encourages infiltration and therefore further deposition so long as material is available.

The reverse process, the gradual removal of valley-fill deposits, requires one or other or a combination of the following causes: a lowering of the drainage outlet (base level), high flood discharges capable of maintaining flow along great lengths of the river, high velocities capable of re-eroding river-bed material, and little infiltration loss. The first provides a point at which gulleying of valley-fill can start. The second requires more frequent flood-producing rain and therefore higher rainfall. The third requires either very high discharges or a steepening of the slope, which would eventually result from a lowering of the drainage outlet. The fourth can be caused in several ways: for instance, a decrease in permeability once the process of re-erosion has removed the looser, less cemented surface material; or increased gradient and velocities giving less time for infiltration. The process will be very slow unless the drainage outlet is lowered, but once it has started it also is self-perpetuating until there is a change in the rainfall and flood régime.

The end result of the removal of valley-fill is terrace formation. The terraces are merely the remnants of various previous positions of the valley-fill surface.

Alluvial terraces are of great interest to archaeologists and not only to those whose concern is with the Palaeolithic period. Although Pleistocene terraces as such, and their mode of formation, lie outside the scope of this book, study of them is relevant, in so far as similar processes have continued into the Holocene, for a proper understanding of the evidence for or against climate change. A widely accepted view is that the chronological sequence of alternating alluviations and down-cutting can be correlated with rainfall changes associated with glaciations and de-glaciations respectively; and that 'pluvials' and heavy alluviations can be equated. I am fully aware that there is an enormous body of expert opinion behind this belief, but there is nowadays a welcome tendency to recognise the complexity of the problem and to admit the importance of sea-level changes and of tectonic movements as factors in both alluviation and down-cutting. Despite this tendency, however, there seems to be an unwillingness to depart from the belief that alluviation results from high or higher rainfall. Many geomorphologists and Paleolithic prehistorians consider that high or higher rainfall was the 'pluvial' low latitude equivalent of glaciation, or that it was at least directly related to the latter.

The belief that there is a direct relationship between climate, expressed in terms of rainfall, and the processes of alluviation and down-cutting is well founded, but the often accepted form of this relationship does not appear to agree with the facts of run-off, erosion, and sedimentation. These beliefs do not take into account the fact that massive erosion today is an arid or semi-arid phenomenon, and do not give sufficient weight to earth movements and sea-level change. As erosional activity is the original source of the deposited material, whether it be derived from primary hill-slope erosion or secondary-re-erosion of former deposits, the massive deposits of alluvium must surely correspond with maxima of erosion. This seems axiomatic as regards the source of the material, and as water was the main agent in both removing the material from its original situations and depositing it elsewhere, the hydrological and hydraulic aspects must be of paramount importance. It is important to note that alluvial terraces of the Pleistocene, about which the following discussion centres, are widely found throughout what are now arid or semi-arid areas.

Some explanation must be found for the enormous quantities of material eroded, as evidenced by the great thickness of deposits. Even under long-sustained semi-arid conditions, it is difficult to believe that the rare floods characteristic of semi-arid torrents could achieve so much. The explanation may well lie in a literally 'grass-roots' approach. During any of the interstadials or interglacials which lasted for a few tens of thousands of years, the vegetation in what are arid zones today adapted itself both in density and in its botanical spectrum to conditions of low, highly variable, and strictly seasonal rainfall. Under such conditions only xerophytic species survive. At situations having a mean annual rainfall of about 200–250 mm. with strictly seasonal distribution, the occasional storms that produce run-off—those whose rainfall intensity is greater than the infiltration capacity of the soil—encounter little resistance to erosion. If sufficiently intense rain occurs before vegetation has had a chance to re-establish itself seasonally and provide a degree of protection, the amount of erosion will be greater than if the rain occurs later in the season. This sort of thing is happening today but, although it is almost everywhere helped by human factors such as over-grazing and by dry-farming in areas where the rainfall does not justify it, the amounts removed are not comparable with those that went to form the alluvial valley-fills of the Pleistocene. Nor does the type of material transported correspond, for today (except along the headwater beds of torrents) the material is mostly the sand, silt, and clay fractions whereas Pleistocene valley-fill is often of boulders and gravels in a matrix of finer materials. Furthermore, the amount of torrent-bed erosion today, although sometimes sufficient to interrupt communications, is not great enough to account for alluviation of the Pleistocene type, even when maintained for tens of thousands of years. The key probably lies in the xerophytic vegetation type and its habit of forming deep-root systems adapted to a search for deep water, rather than a shallow protective root-sod.

As has already been noted, major terrace remnants of Pleistocene valley-fills are a feature of the arid and semi-arid zones. There appears to be reason to believe that the climate during interglacial or interstadial periods was much the same as it is today, so we may believe that in the arid and semi-arid areas the vegetation cover too was very similar. An increase of rainfall during the succeeding glacial or stadial would have increased the density of the existing type of xerophytic vegetation. The way in which the rainfall would have increased can be inferred by study of either a north-south or an altitudinal rainfall profile in the present semi-arid zones. This leads to the conclusion that the increase would be largely achieved through a greater number of storm events: storms would not only occur at closer intervals but over a somewhat longer season. There is no need to postulate higher storm rainfall intensity, and indeed there is reason to believe that intensities are often higher in areas of lower mean rainfall. The increased total duration of rainfall excess, acting on a vegetative cover not intrinsically adapted to take advantage of it, or to give protection, would have resulted in an increase of erosion. The nature of the material transported, with a high proportion of cobbles and gravel, suggests that the soil mantle was fairly rapidly removed first, thus exposing the underlying weathered rock and permitting the more rapid physical weathering of this. The removal of the soil mantle would have tended to reduce the vegetative cover.

If the expression 'Pluvial' is strictly defined as implying a long period during which there was some increase of rainfall of the same type and seasonal distribution as that of today (perhaps an increase of as much as 200 mm. per annum where the mean is now about 200-250 mm. per annum) it is entirely unobjectionable. If the term is allowed to imply different rainfall characteristics and seasonal distribution, it is misleading as far as the non-tropical parts of the world are concerned. Pluvial increases of whatever amount in areas having, either now or previously, rainfall means of 600 mm. per annum or more, and short summer droughts, would have had little erosional effect. Such areas would carry enough shallow-rooted vegetation, and forest cover, to protect the soil. Areas characterised by 250 mm. mean rainfall and the appropriate types of xerophytic vegetation would have been extremely sensitive to increased rainfall until the vegetational spectrum had become adapted to the higher rainfall, through immigration of less xerophytic types. The areas sensitive to increased erosion through failure to adapt quickly to increased rainfall would have lain roughly between the full desert of today, in which water erosion would have occurred farther out into the desert than it now does; and the present-day 500 mm. isohyet. The maximum sensitivity would have been around the 200–250 mm. isohyet of today.

In all these areas, one other factor may have tended towards increased erosion. The southward shift, in the northern hemisphere, of the depression tracks and particularly any tendency for them to move south earlier in the autumn of each year, could have resulted in more autumn convective rain of high intensity. This still happens occasionally. When it does, erosion is considerable, for high intensity rain falls on soil that is afforded little or no protection by plants that are dead and brittle after five or six months of drought, even if those plants have not, in the meantime, been grazed, burnt, or blown away. Increased erosional activity would have continued until the vegetation association had adapted itself, through the immigration of less xerophytic species, to one appropriate to the increased rainfall. This adaptation through immigration could only occur when a source of new species was available, and there must have been some situations in which this basic requirement could not be met at all and where, therefore, heavy erosion would have continued during the long millennia of increased rainfall.

It is not, in fact, easy to visualise any geographical situation where the large-scale immigration of less xerophytic associations would be easy. Wind-borne seeds would ensure the immigration of some new species, but heavy-fruiting plants, although they could have been moved by water, would have immigrated mainly into valley bottoms leaving hill slopes unaffected except very locally. In many cases, therefore, and particularly on hill slopes, the establishment of a vegetative cover that could give protection against higher rainfall would probably have been long delayed by simple logistics and still further delayed by the loss of top-soil.

Thus it seems likely that 'pluvial' alluviation should be equated with the transition period from dry to wetter conditions: and that the 'pluvials' themselves represented a fairly modest increase of the same type of intermittent, fairly intense, seasonal rainfall that characterises the same localities today. This type of rainfall causes flash floods of the kind that carry relatively high sediment loads: they, and the storms producing them, would have been more frequent than they are now, and it follows from this that the frequency of occurrence of a particular peak discharge or a total flood discharge would have increased. What would now be statistically described (in a location where the records extend over a long enough period to make statistical analysis valid) as a flood-peak discharge with an average recurrence period of ten years, might then have had a recurrence period of two years. Whatever the frequency of floods, however, there is no reason to infer that their flashy nature was any different, and so the distances to which they transported solids would have been much the same as they are today.

Much has been made of the shape of alluvial cobbles and gravels, the extent to which their presumed original angularity has been rounded by the process of rolling and attrition, as an indicator of distances of transportation. I think that too much is made of it, for the distance is in fact inexorably set by the distance from the parent source of material in the head waters. Rounding is not, in any case, only a function of distance; it depends on the turbulence of the river, the velocity of flow, the proportion of fine abrasive particles originally present and their manufacture during transport, and on the steepness, section, slope, and crookedness of the river channel. Two or three hours of churning around in a single flash flood can do a great deal of damage to angular particles. It must be remembered too that the bed-load, in which much of this attrition takes place and which, in its turn, acts as an abrasive agent on the underlying stationary or relatively stationary material, does not move as one with the water. The water of a flood of a few hours' duration may travel many miles, but much of the transported solids moves far shorter distances.

4 WATER AND CLIMATE AS AGENTS OF GEOMORPHOLOGY — II

The principal factors controlling deposition of sediments have been described briefly in the previous chapter. It is now worth examining how they operate in practice. Massive deposition takes place when the velocity of flow becomes insufficient to maintain the solids in motion. Cobbles and gravels are deposited at fairly high velocities while sand and silt are deposited at progressively lower velocities. Clay is normally deposited under conditions of no flow. The velocity of flow depends on the slope of the channel, on its roughness, and on what is known as the hydraulic mean depth. The latter is a straightforward geometrical concept, relating the area of cross-section of flow to the cross-sectional length of the contact between the flowing water and its channel. The instantaneous rate of discharge, velocity, channel geometry, and roughness are all interdependent. The roughness of the channel represents a state of equilibrium between the range of velocities that occur and the size of material transported. Increased velocity tends to leave behind only large material and a rougher surface. The rougher surface tends to reduce the velocity.

During any flood, and most particularly during a flash flood, the interrelationship is constantly changing and so, therefore, is the capacity of the flood to move or transport solids. The maximum rate of discharge and maximum sediment capacity may be literally instantaneous, and generally the effectiveness of a flood in transporting coarse material is limited to a short period spanning the peak discharge.

Essentially the building up of gravel alluvium is a prograding activity that cannot extend beyond the point downstream at which vigorous flow stops. With frequent vigorous flows, cobbles and gravels will be more frequently transported to this limit. The limit may be the point where the river-bed gradient flattens on emerging from a steep mountain course: it may be a lake or the sea. It may also be the point at which, with or without change of gradient, the bed-losses owing to infiltration into underlying pervious material reduce the flow beyond its capacity to maintain the movement of solids. The point reached will seldom be the same for any two floods because of differences of discharge.

When deposition of gravels or sand has once started, bed-losses of water into sediments already deposited increasingly limit the distance of sediment transportation. Sudden deposition in this way of large quantities of coarse material possibly accounts for deep gravel and boulder beds in Pleistocene valley-fills. Sometimes deposition of fine materials, by limiting the opportunity for infiltration, assists in the maintenance of long-distance flow and transportation. Channels can be formed either by cutting into older deposits or by the irregular building up of sand and gravel banks. Where deposition is proceeding in this way, with perhaps occasional cutting into earlier deposits, the overall effect, when seen in a vertical section, is of a confusing and often cross-bedded series of gravel beds whose general slope approximates to that of the earlier valley bottom. The whole length of deposits must eventually come to a fairly abrupt downstream end which, in the absence of a lake or sea terminus, takes the form of an alluvial fan. This sequence of events can be seen happening on a smaller and much more intermittent, and therefore slower, scale today and it is absolutely dependent on flash floods. For while such floods are the obvious means of transportation, they are also, but perhaps less obviously, the most plausible explanation of deposition.

It is an interesting point that in the absence of some new factor there seems to be no reason why deposition should not continue, at a reduced tempo, after the massive 'pluvial' deposition. If the more frequent 'pluvial' floods, for all their apparent erosive down-cutting potential, did not in fact cause down-cutting (but very much the reverse), it seems inconceivable that less frequent floods of the same kind should have done so. The explanation may lie partly in the tendency for the sand and silt matrix of gravel alluvia to become cemented with the passage of time by deposition of carbonates, etc., a process that would be aided by less frequent saturation and more aeration. The combination of cemented deposits and of reduced deposition of fresh permeable material would limit the possibility of infiltration. Undoubtedly the loss of water by a river into its pervious bed is one of the principal factors in building up deep alluvium. With reduced infiltration, flow would have been maintained over a greater distance and would more frequently have reached the downstream terminus. Here it could have started gradual headward erosion, but this process by itself seems quite insufficient to account for the massive down-cutting re-erosion of which there is ample evidence.

Two other explanations seem feasible. The first would apply in situations where a fairly rapid vegetational adjustment reduced the supply of sediments while still permitting strong and variable run-off, mostly as flash floods. These, flowing over an increasingly impervious bed, would provide enough water to maintain headward erosion with gradual redeposition of the eroded material further downstream. In certain areas the general retreat of glaciers, with consequently increased discharges from annual snow-melt, may have provided the relatively sediment-free water. The second is that tectonic or epierogenic movement may have altered the river bed slope. This is what has happened and is still happening along the rejuvenating drainage towards the Rift Valley in southern Jordan* and it is what has happened in parts of Baluchistan. Whether the movement flattens or steepens the stream gradient the effect is much the same though the process differs.

Cemented boulder or gravel alluvium is very stable when dry but when wet loses much of its strength and is liable to vertical cleavage. Caves, thought to be of protohistoric age, near Bela in Baluchistan, illustrate this phenomenon. They are situated in vertical cliffs of quaternary conglomerate, a much more stable material than cemented Holocene deposits. Originally each cave consisted of two rooms, one behind the other, as is evident from those that have been discovered intact and the remains of others. Without ever losing

* Burdon, *Handbook of the Geology of Jordan.*

2. Accumulated flood water in the 'fula' at El Fasher has almost entirely evaporated away or been drunk by flocks and herds from miles around.

3. (*Below*) Flood water going to waste in the Arabian sea (a few kilometres down-stream); the flood is subsiding. Twenty-four hours earlier it covered the entire plain.

4. A general view of the rock-cut caves at Mai Gundrani, near where the Kud River debouches onto the north end of the Las Bela plain.

5. A detail of one of the Mai Gundrani caves shows how vertical erosion of the conglomerate rock has cut, and in this case almost entirely removed, the outer chamber.

their vertical form the cliff faces have cut back so that sometimes only a vestige of the outer room remains. I was there immediately after a heavy storm and had the unpleasant experience of seeing what had been a vast vertical slab of rock lying shattered at a point where I had ridden two days earlier.

Flattening of a valley gradient would tend to saturate and soften the alluvium without making it appreciably more permeable, so that headward erosion would be aided. Steepening of the gradient would result in higher velocities with more erosive power. Once headward erosion has started, the probability of flow reaching the erosion head continually increases as there are progressively smaller losses on the way.

In many areas of the world tectonic activity is endemic and it can have operated at any time during the Pleistocene and Holocene: it could also have taken place during periods of maximum alluviation with consequent modification of the alluvial régime. During the glaciations and subsequent deglaciations another similar form of crustal movement known as isostasy occurred in and around glaciated areas. This took the form of tilting in one direction owing to the weight of superimposed ice, or of reverse tilting when the ice subsequently disappeared. As ice-caps were building up, the earth's crust subsided under the weight with compensatory uplift of immediately surrounding areas. As the ice-caps disappeared the movements were reversed. In the first case the effect was to change drainage régimes by increasing the relative difference of land and sea levels. However, most alluvial deposits in glaciated areas and their immediate surroundings are different in their origins from those transported and deposited by floods caused by rain. Ice from the glaciated areas flowed continuously outwards towards the margins, scouring the earth's surface and carrying with it vast quantities of material that gradually became ground down to a form of coarse clay with a certain amount of boulders of more resistant rock. As the margins retreated seasonally the transported material was gradually deposited as moraines roughly along the line of winter advance. When these were formed in valleys they became eventually natural dams behind which ice-melt was stored. Each season of ice-melt brought in some of the transported clay which was deposited in thin laminations known as *varves*. Some ice-melt lakes have left evidence of their former shore lines in the form of gravel beaches: these are a familiar sight in parts of Scotland.

The counting of varves and their identification with material datable by C^{14} or other methods form the basis of varve-chronology.

Varves, moraines, ice-caps, raised beaches are all aspects of geomorphology and they are all intimately connected with water. But whereas seasonal ice-melt, either in the form of seasonal river discharges or variations of lake levels, is susceptible of study by normal hydrological methods, the reasons for the glacial conditions themselves are climatological.

Climate as a whole, and particularly periods of climate change, profoundly affect the earth's surface. Although this operates largely through rainfall or lack of it, rainfall has already been sufficiently discussed and it is time to consider climate itself.

There is a certain degree of correlation everywhere between the complex of phenomena known collectively as climate and the physical scene. Sometimes the correlation is so precise that an experienced person looking at the shape of the country and its drainage, and at its vegetation and surface geology, can deduce with some confidence the approximate rainfall, temperature range, and so on. Certain geomorphological features can be labelled without much hesitation: for instance, the existence of closed drainage basins—those having no natural outlet to the sea—indicate that arid conditions have persisted for very long periods indeed. There is nothing obscure about this: it simply means that such water as enters the basin is not sufficient to overcome evaporation losses. If it were sufficient the lowest part of the basin would sooner or later fill with water to a point where regular overflow would be possible and the overflow would eventually cut an outlet. Wide river beds normally dry, and steep enough to be composed of coarse material, indicate the intermittent occurrence of high run-off. Some of these things give an indication of the order of magnitude of climatic change. The prevalence of closed drainage basins in the deserts of today suggests that any changes have not been of sufficient magnitude to change their desert nature more than marginally.

The evidence of many ice-ages separated by warmer periods, all of varying lengths, is indisputable, and not disputed, evidence of climate change at least in the glaciated areas. There is less agreement as to the nature of the accompanying changes outside these areas—indeed, it is unlikely that there will ever be sufficient reliable evidence to enable people to agree. None the less, certain limiting factors can be assumed and others guessed at with some confidence, particularly if for simplicity's sake the transition periods from warm to cold and back again are ignored. The limiting factor is the continued existence of the two desert or semi-desert belts that follow very roughly the tropics of Cancer and Capricorn. These owe their origin to global atmospheric circulation patterns that are inseparable from the temperature and radiation difference between the equatorial regions and the poles.

A feature of this general circulation is a broad zone of descending (subsident) air on either side of an equatorial zone of unstable ascending air. Whatever the source and original condition of the subsident air it undergoes adiabatic compression as it descends: that is, its pressure increases without its being able to lose or gain heat from outside sources. As a result it becomes warmer and drier. The zones of subsident air roughly correspond with the desert zones. The geomorphology of desert areas shows that they have survived all the changes that caused glaciations, for otherwise the prevalence of enclosed drainage basins is inexplicable. It is probable that both the fundamental causes of glaciations and the direct effect of the extended ice-caps themselves resulted in some displacement of the zone of subsident air towards the Equator and possibly some reduction in the width of this zone. So, along the northern edge of the Sahara-Libyan desert and Arabia, there may have been a slight southward retreat of the desert.

The limiting factors that can be guessed at are much more difficult to assess and are therefore put forward with great reserve. During the northern winter of an ice-age, the effect of the extended ice-caps on atmospheric circulation may have been little different from that of the wide-spread snow-cover of today and I would therefore expect the winter weather to differ from that of the present age mainly in being colder. Increased areas of sea ice could have altered the details of circumpolar air mass circulation fairly considerably. During the northern summer there was a far greater difference from the conditions of today. The extended ice-caps would have tended to maintain large areas of cold high-pressure air throughout the year, and the extent to which this effect was counteracted by summer warmth in the southern parts of the ice-caps cannot even be guessed at. Annual melting of sea ice would have disturbed the pressure distribution to some unknown extent. The disturbances or depressions that now circulate well to the north in the summer would have been deflected southward, but the amount of deflection would have been limited by the zone of stable subsident air. On the whole it seems probable that the zone traversed by depressions was not merely shifted southward but also became more narrow. For this deflection to have any significance as increased rainfall it is necessary to assume that disturbances were as frequent then as now and crowded into a rather narrower zone. There is some evidence that rainfall amounts in northern Mediterranean latitudes, for instance, were greater during the ice-ages and this may be the reason. The effect in southern Mediterranean latitudes may well have been to create a rather narrower zone of transition between those areas having fairly regular all the year round rainfall and the desert.

The inference to be drawn from this is that probably the desert-margin area in the Middle East had more rainfall than it has today. I do not think there is enough evidence to form an estimate of the amount of difference in a given place, but the following illustrations may give an idea of the kind of difference to expect. In northern Jordan I would guess that areas now enjoying a mean rainfall of 500 mm. per annum, practically all occurring between October and April, would then have enjoyed perhaps 800 mm. mean rainfall of which a significant part—perhaps as much as 100 mm. on an average—would have occurred irregularly in the summer months. These conditions would have supported hill vegetation similar to that of the Alban Hills near Rome today. In areas nearby now having 300 mm. mean annual rainfall the increase would probably have been somewhat less, to perhaps 500 mm., and the vegetation could have been like that of similar situations in Calabria. Out in what is now the Syrian desert, with a notional mean rainfall of about 50 to 100 mm. per annum, the increase would have been less again and I would guess that the rainfall was then about 200 to 250 mm. with steppe vegetation. In the south of Jordan the effect would, I think, have been less marked so that a place like Wadi Musa, near Petra, with 200 mm. mean rainfall today, would probably not have had any more than 300 mm. then. In the north of Jordan sporadic summer rain might have occurred, but I doubt whether there would have been an appreciable amount south of Wadi Musa. These are only tentative illustrations to give some idea of the nature of the changes caused by glaciations in one archaeologically important area.

In certain situations such as that of Jericho and the whole of the western margin of the Indus Valley the effect of glaciation would have been small, for these are all in classical rain-shadow situations. Moisture-laden air from the west descends as soon as it has passed over the barriers of the Judaean hills or the mountains of Baluchistan as the case may be, and undergoes adiabatic heating and drying. This effect is also known as *Föhn* effect.

I have devoted some space to consideration of glacial climate in the Middle East because, although I fully agree that there has been change, the amount and significance of that change should not be exaggerated. Many things stemmed from it that could hardly have done so if it were greater than I have suggested.

So far I have dealt with possible climatic conditions during the ice-ages. It is of very great importance, and fortunately less a matter of guesswork, to determine when conditions returned to those of today. If the researches and conclusions of Milankovitch, of whom I shall have more to say, and of those who have elaborated his theory, are well founded, the radiation maximum responsible for the interglacial or interstadial in which we live had already been reached in about 10,000 B.C. This maximum is known as the *Alleröd* oscillation. For several thousand years before that time conditions favourable to deglaciation had been gradually increasing, and the fact that ice-caps had not then retreated, and did not finally retreat until long afterwards can only be explained in terms of the colossal amount of heat required to convert the accumulated ice to water (that is, the latent heat of fusion of ice). The evidence of sea-levels suggests that melting of the ice did not really get under way until about 9000 B.C. Archaeological evidence suggests that present sea-levels were not established until about 4000 B.C. at the earliest. Some time between these limits the climate of today became established.

The reason for deflection of depressions towards the Equator in summer time during any ice-age was the existence right through the summer of vast areas of ice that created corresponding areas of high atmospheric pressure. As soon as the area of summer ice had shrunk to somewhere near its present limits the reason for this deflection disappeared. There is evidence that the extent of continental permanent ice had already shrunk enormously by 8000 B.C. and it is probable that the atmospheric circulation of today was established about 7000 B.C. There is certainly evidence that by about this date the climate of the Middle East was generally that of today with all the enormous degree of short-term variation implicit in that statement. The lag in the recovery of sea-level would have been caused by the slow melting of ice-caps on Antarctica, Greenland, and all the permafrost areas of northern Europe, Asia and Canada.

The geomorphological effect of this change was expressed through isostasy which has already been described, and through the quite distinct phenomenon of *eustasy*. This is a term used to describe the state of ocean level in relation to the amount of water withdrawn from hydrologic circulation into ice storage. It has been estimated that during glaciations the amount of water so withdrawn was sufficient to lower the ocean level by as much as 60 to 100 metres for the most recent glaciation. The evidence of sea-level changes has been used not only to deduce ice-age climatic change, which is self-evident, but to identify and give dates to a number of post-glacial climatic phases. This evidence is considered in some detail later. For the moment let it suffice to say that both the evidence and the conclusions drawn from it are contradictory. The sub-divisions into a number of phases of the time that has elapsed since the last glaciation may have served a useful purpose. At least the belief in them is an implicit admission of the importance of climate in the environment. Unfortunately the phases with their rather clumsy names—pre-Boreal, Boreal, Atlantic, sub-Boreal, sub-Atlantic—have acquired with time a certain authority as a universal dating framework.

Many workers in prehistoric environment go further and claim that there is evidence for a period known as the Post-glacial Climatic Optimum, to give it its full title. This concept is even less supported by the evidence: and indeed the various dates ascribed to it cover a range of so many millennia that they alone condemn it. For it cannot be over-emphasised that climate is a world-wide phenomenon. If, therefore, the dates of allegedly different phases show not even approximate world-wide agreement, the environmental evidence of change has probably been misinterpreted. This brief digression into a much disputed field leads to further consideration of sea-level change and its effects, and to a review of the underlying causes of both it and climate change.

It should be clear from what has been said earlier that in referring to sea-level change at any place I mean the change of *relative* level of land and sea at this point. This can be the result of many complementary and sometimes opposing factors. There is first and foremost eustasy, which alone of all such factors is both world-wide and directly linked to world-wide climate change; there is isostasy, which only operated around glaciated areas, sometimes reinforcing and sometimes opposing the universal effect of eustasy; and there is and always has been, particularly in tectonically active parts of the world, crustal movement of irregular occurrence and in either direction, entirely unconnected with glaciation.

During the building up of ice-caps isostasy, by upwarping coastlines, sometimes accentuated and accelerated the fall of sea-level in relation to the land. When the ice-caps melted the reverse process sometimes accelerated the relative rise of sea-level.

It follows from this that anything approaching an accurate estimate of the eustatic effect can only be obtained by looking for evidence remote from glaciated areas and where movements of the earth's crust are likely to have been minimal. While there are many places to choose from there is seldom any direct incentive to search; for if datable and unequivocal evidence still survives it is now deep under the sea, where anything of obvious archaeological interest has probably long disappeared. Just how deep, is at present anybody's guess, but the simple arithmetic of glaciation can throw some light on the problem. It is generally agreed that about 80 per cent of the earth's surface is occupied by oceans so that their total area is in the neighbourhood of 1,300 million square kilometres. The present area of permanent glaciation on land has been estimated at about 40 million square kilometres, although I should prefer the more conservative figure of 30 million. I have not seen reliable estimates of the total additional area of permanent land ice during the last glaciation, but would not expect this to have exceeded about 15 million square kilometres. The total area of permanent land ice at that time might therefore have been somewhere between 45 and 55 million square kilometres. For simplicity let us assume a figure of 50 million, or one twenty-sixth of the total ocean area.

From this rough calculation it appears that an average thickness of 26 metres of ice all over the glaciated part of all land masses would be required to account for one metre eustatic drop in sea-level. The frequently quoted figure of 100 metres eustatic drop in sea-level would have required an average ice thickness of nearly two and a half kilometres. This is by no means impossible for, assuming 20,000 years of accumulation, it implies an average net increase per annum of only 130 mm. Taking into account all forms of ablation (loss of ice by both seasonal melting and direct evaporation), this would probably represent a mean precipitation of the equivalent of a little over 200 mm. of rain. The present polar regions could be classed as arid on the basis of their precipitation, so there is reason to accept this rate of accumulation.

Although an eustatic drop of 100 metres appears to be of the right order it must be emphasised that the effect of isostasy cannot be estimated. So wherever actual measurements of former sea-level have agreed approximately with this figure they may require to be considerably amended when corrected for isostasy.

An indication of the possible scale of isostasy results from consideration of former beach levels in Italy now raised 100 metres or more above sea-level. If isostasy were to be ignored, the implication of these beaches would be that during some warm interglacial period the present quantity of permanent land ice was reduced sufficiently to account for a sea-level rise of 100 metres. On the basis of 40 million square kilometres of present ice, a thickness of 3,300 metres of present ice would have to disappear. At a guess this would involve the total disappearance of all present permanent ice and that the even higher ocean levels, of which the higher terraces are said to be evidence, would have been impossible. There is of course evidence that in geological epochs long before the Pleistocene, the present polar regions had tropical or sub-tropical vegetation, but so far as I know there has never been any suggestion that they were ever deglaciated during the Pleistocene.

Probably, therefore, the Mediterranean raised beaches have to be explained in other ways. For instance, if the Mediterranean had been at any time during the Pleistocene separated from the Atlantic by an isthmus where the Straits of Gibraltar now are it would have had its own isolated eustatic balance. (There is no evidence that I know of that this was the case.) The proportion of sea area to land area draining into it, in the case of an isolated Mediterranean, would have been far smaller than the global four to one ratio of the oceans to the whole land surface, and the eustatic effect would have been much greater. In fact, it is conceivable that a Gibraltar isthmus, if it ever existed, was converted into a seaway simply by sustained overflow of an unduly heightened Mediterranean. Another possible explanation is that the raised beaches are due to a combination of isostasy and crustal movement, but their comparative regularity around Italy makes this unlikely. The argument is mainly of value in showing how careful one has to be to try to isolate eustatic effects and how nearly impossible it is to do so.

A secondary geomorphological effect of sea-level change, and one of very great importance, was the resulting change in drainage outlets. Lowering of sea-level not only lowered the drainage outfalls of all rivers flowing to the sea, but profoundly affected ground-water level around all coasts. Subsequent raising of sea-levels inhibited down-cutting of river beds in their lower reaches and raised ground-water levels. These are facts that are largely independent of the amount of sea-level change.

The theory of Milankovitch, mentioned earlier, is of importance in providing dating milestones for a major agency of climate change, possibly the only agency. Its acceptance precludes any possibility of explaining minor post-glacial climate changes (and alleged short-term sea-level changes) in terms analogous to those explaining the ice-ages. A brief examination of it and of a recent strong attack on it are therefore very relevant to the question of climate phases, which will be considered later.

It must immediately be admitted that Milankovitch's theory is by no means universally accepted. In one of the most authoritative recent works on prehistoric environment, *Environment and Archaeology* by Professor Karl W. Butzer, the author declares himself against the theory. Butzer both sums up and criticises the basic concept in one sentence which is worth quoting. He describes the concept as one of 'constant total solar radiation with variations in time of the latitudinal and seasonal distribution, the background being provided by certain periodic changes of the axis and orbit of the earth which obviously did not begin with the Pleistocene'. I would have preferred to describe it as an explanation of long-term variation in the amount of solar energy received at any point on the earth's surface, due to certain periodic changes of the earth's axis and orbit against a background of constant total solar radiation.

Butzer's statement that the changes obviously did not begin with the Pleistocene cannot be left unchallenged; for something quite clearly did begin with the Pleistocene, which is distinguished from previous geological epochs largely by the series of glaciations that Milankovitch explains. Something fundamental must have initiated the change to Pleistocene conditions and it seems reasonable to accept that whatever this event was it set off the periodic changes (or some of them) that Milankovitch has identified. Far more fundamental changes have occurred between the beginning of the Pleistocene and that much more remote period when the polar regions carried dense vegetation, probably because they were not then polar.

The periodicities taken into account by Milankovitch, that affected the incidence of solar energy on a given point of the earth's surface, concern the variations in the angle of the ecliptic, the shift in the date of perihelion and what Butzer refers to as an obscure variation in the eccentricity of the earth's orbit. I suspect that this last is not obscure to astronomers though I do not pretend to understand it myself. Obscure or not it appears to be the least significant of the periodic variations. The most significant is the variation in the angle of the ecliptic, the angle between the earth's axis and the plane in which it moves around the sun. At the moment this is about 67°.

These changes, whose existence has been verified by observation and mathematics, have different periodicities so that their combined effect is continually changing. At present perihelion, the date on which the earth in its orbit is closest to the sun, falls in the northern winter. The effect of its occurrence during the northern summer over a long period would be to reinforce slightly any tendency to colder northern winters arising from the other changes. The over-all major oscillations in radiation are preponderantly due to changes in the angle of the ecliptic, the other changes having mainly the effect of modifying the peaks and amplitudes of these oscillations. The most recent in the series of radiation maxima is the Alleröd oscillation already referred to, and dated to about 10,000 B.C. Since that time the radiation received along any latitude of the earth has decreased. M. Combier at the Congresso Internazionale delle Scienze Preistoriche e Protostoriche at Rome in 1961, illustrated his paper on 'Chronologie et Systématique du Moustérien Occidental' with the radiation curve for the last 100,000 years. The curve is based on Milankovitch's theory with corrections based on more recent and accurate data. His curve reveals the extreme environmental importance of the variations of radiation. Taking as his standard latitude that of 65° N, he shows that at a radiation maximum the effect is as if the latitude were reduced to 61° N; while at a radiation minimum the effect is as if the latitude were increased to about 74° N. The range of variation of radiation received during a whole cycle is equivalent therefore to 13° of latitude or about 1,450 kilometres. It does not follow from his curve that the range of variation is as great at lower latitudes, but assuming that it is of the same general order the effect of the whole range of variation could correspond to the climatic difference between London and Rome.

Butzer raises one other objection which must be challenged. He states that 'strong evidence favours the synchronononous nature of climatic changes and oscillations on both the nothern and southern hemisphere in conflict with the basic requirements of the astronomical theory'. But is there conflict? The major peaks of high and low radiation follow the variations in perturbation of the earth's axis. Their amplitude can be slightly increased or decreased by changes in seasonal occurrence of perihelion and in that 'obscure' variation of the ellipticity of the earth's orbit. The major factor, perturbation of the earth's axis, must be synchronous for both hemispheres, for each hemisphere must experience to exactly the same extent each year the increase or decrease of solar radiation due to the current degree of perturbation.

The Milankovitch theory demonstrates the lack of global cause for climatic change in the postglacial. If it and all the data on which it is based are wrong, we are left with no satisfactory alternative explanation for glaciations, which is bad enough, and with nothing whatever to guide us in the postglacial. Even the opponents of the theory do not dispute the premises and it can be said that they are right so far as modern knowledge goes, and that they probably take acount of all known phenomena affecting radiation received on the earth apart from any arising in the sun itself. The known variations in solar radiation, due to sun spots, for instance, are of short periodicity and do not appear to have any trend. Their short periodicity seems absolutely to exclude them as causes of glaciations.

The claim of Professor Butzer (which appears as a footnote in his book) cannot be sustained—that no meteorologist or climatologist at the World Meteorological Organisation—

UNESCO Symposium on change of climate (Rome, October 1961) seriously considered the astronomical radiation curve. He himself certainly opposed the radiation theory, but the vast majority of contributors to the Symposium were concerned with more recent periods to which the theory is not applicable. R. W. Fairbridge in his paper says of the Milankovitch hypothesis '... we do not find that this cyclicity is out of harmony with the record of Quarternary climatic events'. And when Butzer states that there is 'almost general reservation of Pleistocene stratigraphers and meteorologists today about Milankovitch's radiation curves' he is surely confusing normal scientific scepticism with the outright rejection that he himself appears to advocate.

5 WATER AS AN ECOLOGICAL FACTOR — I

Hydrology, as an applied science, and water as an agent of geomorphological change, have been introduced in the last two chapters. I hope that it will have emerged from this introduction that hydrology and geomorphology are inextricably mixed. The first is essential in explaining much of the second, while some aspects of the second provide essential data for studying the first.

Mention has already been made of the role of vegetation in geomorphological change, and I will now try to demonstrate that the interdependence of hydrology on the one hand and botany and zoology on the other is as important as the link already established with geomorphology.

Ecology is the study of living organisms of every kind against the background of their physical inanimate environment; of the interdependence of various forms of life; and of the feed-back effect of life on the inanimate environment. The whole relationship can be pictured in various ways. In the following diagram the base of each arrow indicates the active agent and the head of it indicates the thing affected.

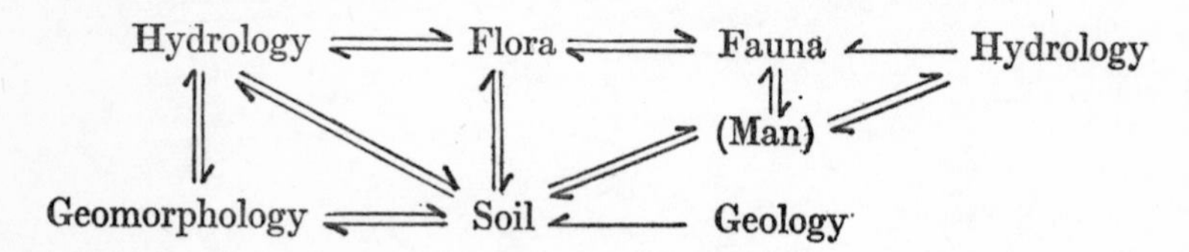

The popular expression 'balance of nature' is another way of describing ecology, although it is generally used only in the restricted sense of the balance between floral and faunal species. I have intentionally omitted direct reference to climate in this diagram, which therefore represents only the interplay of various ecological factors against a background of constant climate. The diagram could be extended to show climate as entering at every point of the diagram. Secular change of climate could produce a change in every single factor and all the relationships would be forced to adjust themselves. The extent of the adjustments would depend on the extent of climate change. Most are two-way relationships: that between hydrology and fauna is one-way until man comes into the picture. Hydrology, in the sense of the distribution of drinking water in time and space, has almost as decisive an effect on faunal distribution as does availability of vegetation, but no animal other than man has any effect on the space and time distribution of water. The link between geology and soil is evidently one-way—the creation of soil from parent rock—if one accepts that the process of recreation of sedimentary rock from soil is part of geomorphology.

This chapter concentrates on the complex relationships between Soil, Flora, Fauna, and Hydrology, but it must be remembered that the geomorphological link is operating at the same time.

In any system of interdependent factors it is difficult to know where to enter. There was a similar difficulty in the case of the hydrologic cycle. I propose to select soil, quite arbitrarily, as the point of entry while stressing that its condition at the moment of entry is already a product of the cycle.

Soils are the source of all the minerals which go to the formation of plant life and, through it directly or indirectly, of animal life. Their efficiency as a source of plant food depends on many things: they must contain all the minerals required and must be free of toxic substances; they must contain the minerals in a soluble form; they must be capable of absorbing and retaining water for the solution of the minerals; they may have to contain chemical substances to assist in the solution of minerals or be capable of producing such substances with the help of the roots of vegetation; they must be of a texture that permits roots to explore and benefit from them; they may be relatively acid or alkaline in their reaction only within the limits that plants can tolerate; they must combine their capacity to absorb and retain water with the ability to be drained and aerated; they must somehow be capable of replacing those of their minerals that are lost through leaching or through being consumed by vegetarian animals.

With so many requirements it seems surprising at first that soils capable of supporting plants have not only been created in such vast quantities but have also survived. As almost any soil contains the essential minerals for some kind of plant life the prime requirement is water. This makes the minerals available and transports them through the plant structure to be photo-synthesised into organic plant material by combination with atmospheric carbon dioxide. So I will start with a hypothetical sterile soil of reasonably fine texture such as might be deposited from a river in flood, apply water to it and follow through a hypothetical sequence of events. The seeds of herbs and trees are assumed to be present having either been deposited by the same flood action, borne in by the wind, dropped by birds, or carried on the feet or fur of animals. Water is then applied either by another flood or by precipitation.

The cycle of growth, maturity, fruiting and leaf fall follows. Minerals are drawn from the soil and fall back eventually, diminished only by what has been eaten or blown away or used by man, for instance as firewood. Undisturbed by wind, water, animals, or man, the original sterile soil gradually changes its structure and becomes a loam with an increasing content of fine organic matter. This last builds up until a rough balance exists between its disintegration by soil bacteria and the amount added by leaf fall, etc. In the process the reaction of the soil tends to become relatively more acid whatever the original minerals present. A point can be reached where either this acidity or increasing saturation with water, or both, inhibits the action of soil bacteria. Partial saturation can result from plentiful rain falling on a soil that has become increasingly retentive of water because dead vegetation has accumulated faster than bacteria can decompose it. Relatively acid soils favour some plant species at the expense of others and are more rapidly formed under conditions of high rainfall. They form more quickly and deeply under thick forest cover, which is to some extent another way of saying the same thing. We instinctively and rightly associate dense vegetation and thick forest with high rainfall. We could equally well associate them with evapo-transpiration low enough to leave a constant surplus of water to maintain growth.

Forest trees have a radically different effect from that of shallow rooted vegetation, and so do most plants adapted to very dry conditions (xerophytes). For both trees and xerophytes, with their deep-ranging root systems, draw a lot of their mineral requirements from great depths while still delivering them eventually to the surface as leaf fall. Forests therefore tend to enrich the mineral content of the top-soil when left undisturbed. Xerophytes would in theory do much the same but for their dry habitats, swept often by strong winds that are hardly resisted by their thin vegetation, and the removal as dust of what otherwise might gradually become loam. Ants and other small creatures eat what is left behind by the wind and larger animals, and though they undoubtedly produce tiny quantities of organic matter it is quite insufficient to create a good loamy soil. The effects of low rainfall are therefore generally aggravated by a soil whose structure is not adapted to the retention of moisture.

Soils that are subjected to low seasonal rainfall and to many months of summer drought can, in the natural state, only bear the xerophytic type of vegetation that can survive these conditions. Under irrigation they can of course be made to do all sorts of unnatural things. It is worth noting in passing that practically all our crops of cereals and pulses are descended from cultigens that developed naturally in arid and semi-arid lands. The characteristic arid-zone alternation of a season of highly variable and often inadequate rainfall, with five or six months of absolute drought and often great heat, results in characteristic soils that can be recognised by a soil scientist. Sometimes when such soils have been buried by later deposits, which may result from floods or landslides, or which may have been brought from far away by the wind, the characteristic structure can still be recognised when test-pits or borings bring the material to the new surface. The soil scientist can then say with some confidence what general type of climate existed when the soil was formed.

But a word of warning is necessary. Arid-zone soils occur within a fairly wide compass of combinations of rainfall, length of seasonal drought, temperature range and potential evaporation: a compass probably as great as, if not greater than, that which covered the change from glacial to interglacial conditions at a particular place. A very low mean annual rainfall at latitude 40° N can probably support at least as much vegetation as 50 per cent more rainfall at 25° N if the altitudes and distances from sea coasts are about the same, because evapo-transpiration losses at the lower latitude tend to cancel out the rainfall advantages. When, as happens in certain zones marginal to deserts, there are two annual seasons of rainfall of entirely different origin, the ecological effect will be more favourable than if the same mean annual total was all received in one season. This rather odd effect is observed in the archaeologically interesting area of Baluchistan, and is worth examining. In the Jhalawan district of Baluchistan the mean annual rainfall is 200 mm., divided more or less equally between winter rain caused by Mediterranean-type depressions and summer rains associated with the inter-tropical front. Such data as are available suggest that the frequency of occurrence of half the seasonal total is about once in nine years in each case. The probability of both seasons having half their mean within one period of twelve months is therefore one in eighty-one. If the whole of the 200 mm. mean rainfall fell in one season only, experience elsewhere suggests that the probability of receiving half the mean would be about one in twenty. So the probability of the deficiency associated with half the mean rainfall is four times as great in the case of single-season rainfall. Combinations of any other proportions of seasonal rainfall, for example one-third of winter rainfall, that together give half the annual total, give combined probabilities that are never less favourable. The effect can be expressed in another way. Rainfall of different origins divided into two annual seasons has the same ecological effect as about 50 per cent more mean annual rainfall concentrated into one season, for the same place.

When attempting to deduce rainfall from existing or buried surface soils (palaeosols) it must also be remembered that an area denuded of vegetation by any agency—grazing, fire, deforestation by man, a succession of locust years—will form less soil than one carrying the vegetation normal to its rainfall. A single long-sustained period of drought can alter the whole process of soil formation for many years after it without having any appreciable effect on the long-term rainfall mean. It is clear that there is need for great caution in using soil science for more than the identification of climate type. For this, particularly in the case of arid climates, it is invaluable.

In wetter areas similar care is necessary in distinguishing between the effects of higher rainfall and a high water-table. To some extent the latter is of course a product of the former, but it is far more dependent on drainage which, in its turn, is extremely sensitive to changes of slope including those arising from erosion, and to changes of drainage base-level. In many coastal sites rising sea-level in the post-glacial would have had an effect that otherwise could only be achieved by much increased rainfall.

The simple links between soil and flora, and flora and soil, have been sufficiently explored. It is clear that hydrology enters into both, and the effect of hydrology on soil is seen to be an integral part of the process. The reverse effect, that of the combination of soil and flora on hydrology, has to some extent already been covered in the chapter on hydrology.

As there is wide-spread belief that planting of forests can change climate let us deal with this first. Without irrigation, the creation of forests where little or nothing grew before can only be achieved where the rainfall is already above a certain minimum depending on the type or types of tree selected. The density of planting, or at least the density at which trees will flourish, depends on the combination of rainfall and ground-water available to them. In practically all situations this means that they are dependent on the mean of the rainfall, the extremes on either side of the mean being modified by the storage effect of the earth. They will not grow densely unless the mean rainfall is sufficient for their particular needs, and unless they do so, the amount of water that they transpire into the atmosphere will be small. It will in any case be limited to what is available, and as all that is available from shallow depths would be evaporated and transpired if the trees were not there, all the trees can add is the water that their deep-root systems can bring to the surface. This might initially be significant, but the roots are not exploring an inexhaustable reservoir so that a balance is soon reached with the water-table lowered. In semi-arid countries the transpired water is lost into air that may have anything between about 15 and 50 per cent relative humidity, and it would be a near miracle if, as a result of convection, the tiny additional contribution of moisture even succeeded in forming a few scattered fair weather cumulus clouds. If an enormous area, bare of trees simply because they have been cut and eaten but otherwise capable of supporting good forest, were replanted, the additional effect of trees, as compared with the fairly dense maquis to which such an area would have been reduced, might conceivably be such as to encourage more rain. But it is inconceivable that the rain should fall except by chance on the area planted, and then only on the down-weather part of it. Very large areas of irrigation would have no more effect. I am not overlooking the important oasis micro-climate effect of irrigated areas. But this does not create rain: rather, it reduces evapo-transpiration by producing a more humid atmosphere locally.

Vegetation does have an effect on hydrology but not, in my opinion, on rainfall to any extent. It affects infiltration, evapo-transpiration, and run-off, and deep-rooted species can have such an effect on ground-water that the discharges of springs can be much reduced. In fact, afforestation can be a mixed blessing where water is scarce, and it is sometimes doubtful whether its effect in protecting the soil is not more than offset by the amount of water wasted in transpiration, unless the trees are intrinsically valuable.

As I am treading on ground that is literally covered with highly complicated forms of life that can only be properly understood by botanists or zoologists who have spent years in their study, I have to tread very warily. An interest in gardening or in wild flowers is no more a preparation for botany than a similar interest in weather-forecasting is for hydrology. My only excuse for bringing botany into the picture at all is that it has a strong link with, and dependence on, water. So, with apologies in advance to any of my botanist friends who may read this, I will try to avoid solecisms and keep to what is relevant.

The soil and climate of any particular place on the earth's surface carries a mixed assortment of plants, or of plants and trees, that is sometimes referred to as an 'association'. Even without man's interference the association is intimately dependent on the fauna that, in turn, are associated with it. These range from the earthworms and other burrowing small creatures that work the soil and the larger creatures such as moles that prey on them, through caterpillars and other insects and the birds that prey on them, to birds, mammals, and reptiles that eat the leaves, roots, and fruits and are in turn preyed upon by others. They all live in a finely adjusted balance. Too many insect-eating birds due to a lack of bird predators could reduce the population of useful insects that help in pollination and so reduce the supply of fruits on which other birds or mammals depend. Too few insect-eating birds could result in plagues of caterpillars and severe damage to certain plant species. Nowadays man, in what often seems a greedy attempt to apply factory methods to cultivation, all too frequently makes uncontrolled use of insecticides and hormone weed-killers. The insecticides not only kill off temporarily a large part of the insect population but also, either directly or through starvation, reduce the bird population that normally controls them, with a chain reaction effect on bird predators that are similarly deprived of their prey. The matter does not stop there, for surviving insects with their capacity to lay hundreds or thousands of eggs can make a much quicker come-back than the birds. Unless, therefore, this senseless 'genocide' is maintained to a point where all insects are destroyed along with everything dependent on them, the last state could well be worse than the first. However, the subject has been more eloquently dealt with by others and is only relevant here as an extreme example of what happens when some new or unusual factor upsets the balance—and the whole faunal-floral interdependence is sketched in mainly to avoid accusation of being over-preoccupied with the role of climate.

In any floral association there is a tendency (qualified as necessary by the varying impact on it of its associated fauna), for the component species to establish a certain rough numerical balance one with another. All the individuals of all the species are in constant competition for soil, moisture, and light. Their methods of competition vary. Some put down deep roots to avoid the strenuous competition in the top layers of soil; some germinate earlier in the year and get their growth cycle completed before others have made a serious start; some grow tall in order to reach the light while others blanket the ground with low growth that inhibits competitors; some only flourish when the season is drier than usual, others when it is wetter. For any given situation a stable association is known as the climax. The climax is, at least in theory, dominated by the trees in it because of the advantages of their deep-rooted systems, and this applies right down the scale of dryness to tundra or steppe as the case may be. Tundra is almost treeless, possibly because of permafrost: steppe generally carries tree species but these are so stunted by lack of water (or the too-frequent attentions of hungry camels) that they are like small bushes.

Climaxes, therefore, are often named after their most numerous tree species. Climaxes have been thrust into the archaeological limelight by recent work on pollen-analysis, and the frequency with which change of climax is equated with climate change is proof of the importance attached by botanists to climate and particularly to its wetness and temperature range.

The temperature aspect is important enough to justify fairly detailed examination in order to demonstrate the need for a sense of proportion. It has sometimes been claimed that post-glacial climate phases have been characterised by changes in mean annual temperature of as much as 3°C. Apart from the highly conjectural nature of such claims the effect in terms of climate can only be guessed at. A place with a typical continental-type climate with cold winters and hot summers may have a mean annual temperature exactly the same as that of a place having an oceanic climate with mild winters and cool summers, but neither the layman nor the expert would say that the climates are the same or even similar. Most so-called mean temperatures are not anything of the kind. Observations, except where there are continuously recording instruments, are made at predetermined hours of the day. Sometimes they are made at internationally determined hours. An example of this can be seen any day in those newspapers that publish the temperatures in foreign cities and resorts: for instance, all European reports give the temperature at noon G.M.T.

The *average* temperature of each twenty-four-hour period is calculated from the two or more observations made; the more observations there are during each day the nearer this approaches the mean temperature of the day. The *average* temperature for each month or year or season is calculated from the series of average daily temperatures making up the period. A 'mean' annual temperature calculated in this way can be as much wide of the mark as each of the 'mean' daily temperatures. It is possible that sometimes the mean temperature of a place today, derived from a continuously recording instrument at that place, is compared with the average temperature of past times, derived in the original rather arbitrary manner. There can be and often is a significant difference between the mean and the average.

As in the case of rainfall, the range of variation of temperature at any place can be very considerable although the mode of variation is entirely different; on the whole, the range of variation of either mean or average annual temperature is more than one order of magnitude smaller than that of mean annual rainfall.

I have already shown how rainfall means are a statistical convenience that can entirely obscure the real characteristics of the rainfall. The same can happen with temperatures. A long period of hard frost in a place where its occurrence is rare will not necessarily have any effect on the mean temperature of the year in which it occurs, particularly if it is offset by unusually hot summer weather. But its ecological effect can be considerable and so can that of a long heat wave superimposed on the drought that almost invariably accompanies it.

So if we are to use the same statistical convenience in a prehistoric context it must be done cautiously and with the knowledge that then as now extreme events were of far greater significance than averages or means. With this in mind let us examine a little more deeply the question of whether a mean annual temperature increase or decrease of 3°C, if it existed, was relevant or significant. It seems to me that its relevance is improbable for the range of variation is of the same order as, for instance, that experienced during the 150-year period A.D. 1811 to 1960 at Copenhagen. That and similar evidence from other places seems to dispose of its relevance. Its significance is really impossible to judge, for if mean temperatures conceal the significance of temperature change in the period in which we are living and of which the details are available, how can they possibly tell us anything about remote periods? For that matter, how can they possibly be estimated with any chance of accuracy for remote periods?

However, some idea of the ecological significance of such a temperature change can perhaps be deduced from the range of mean annual temperature within which climaxes survive today. The data from Copenhagen quoted earlier has not resulted in climax change, and the range of mean annual temperatures within which various climaxes flourish in Italy is slightly greater. So I think it has to be conceded that vegetation climaxes are probably too tolerant, as far as temperature goes, for there to be any easily discernible climax change within the range of temperature change postulated.

When we come to consider wetness—that is, rainfall and relative humidity—no one has seriously attempted to ascribe a quantitative measure of greater wetness to those early climate phases that were said to have been distinguished in this way. The range of variation of rainfall between one year and another, one season and another, at any place, is almost certainly at least one order of magnitude greater than the difference between the rainfalls in the so-called Atlantic and Boreal phases, at the same place.

It is rather difficult to be precise about climaxes, even for botanists, because it is almost impossible to find examples of association that have not been completely distorted by man. But one can compare existing climaxes that are more or less artificial and get some idea of the great tolerance of climatic conditions that characterises them. Beech climax covers much of the Apennines in Italy at altitudes that are under snow almost every winter for several months: all the Apennine ski-resorts are in Beech-climax country. The same beech (or at least one indistinguishable by its pollen) grows in much of southern England. The combined effects of a number of climatic parameters are obviously ecologically about the same in each case but no one would suggest that the climates are similar.

It seems, therefore, that even the identification of climate *types* from vegetation climaxes has to be undertaken with great caution, and when all other factors are eliminated a change of climax could at best be described in terms of a wide range of combinations of rainfall-humidity, temperature, and their modes of variation.

The difficulty of eliminating the other factors is well illustrated in the Beech-climax area of Italy. Without any change of climate the areas of beech forest are rapidly becoming smaller. This is because over most of the areas the laws that exist to protect forest lands are difficult to enforce. I do not mean that there is wholesale plunder but rather that sporadic uncontrolled cutting proceeds faster than regeneration. In the past the relatively easy upper slopes were probably systematically deforested in order to provide grazing for sheep, but the soil is not everywhere holding its own. It is remarkable, in fact, how the precipitous slopes that are mostly still forested contain more soil in deep pockets dispersed among scree and boulders than the tops which are now largely reduced to rock and gravel with sparse vegetation.

6 WATER AS AN ECOLOGICAL FACTOR — II

It is mainly in the context of ecology that it is important to assess the effect of climate change. The arguments for and against this are considered in later chapters, but I propose to anticipate my conclusions in order to have an arbitrary background for a more specific approach to the hydrology-ecology link. My conclusions, reached after critically reviewing the available evidence, are that there has been no ecologically significant secular climate change since about 7000 B.C. and only a very minor and possibly insignificant change since a millennium earlier.

Assuming for the moment, therefore, that this has already been substantiated, that part of the ecological environment of the period from 7000 B.C. that is represented by rainfall, temperature, evaporation, and other factors, can be inferred from today's data provided that every possible allowance is made for changes induced by man and animals, and for the effect of the quite extraordinary range of variation of some hydrological parameters, particularly rainfall, that occurs over short periods. To some extent biotic factors, such as fire of which man is so often the trigger, are favoured or inhibited by dryness or wetness. Fire is favoured for obvious reasons by dryness irrespective of man's interference: it is inhibited by well-distributed rainfall.

Man's effect on his environment is now generally taken into account, but the vagaries of rainfall are not. The opinion of a distinguished meteorologist, R. C. Sutcliffe (at the Rome Symposium on Climate Change), is worth quoting:

> Fluctuations on this scale [of a few weeks superimposed on the annual cycle] certainly exist and we do not need to look for an extraneous cause, but there is also the

variation in seasonal weather from year to year, one of the most remarkable facts of climate. Does this need a cause? The question is vital for our understanding. . . . From the internal evidence, especially the large magnitude of the year-to-year variations and the relatively small magnitude of any likely extraneous disturbances, I suspect that the year-to-year variations are indeed built-in characteristics of the system . . . extraneous factors, whether sun-spots or sea temperature, need have no controlling significance.

Let us examine the climatic parameters quantitatively taking the two principal ones that, between them, condition most of the others; that is, temperature and rainfall. Secular mean temperature changes in historical times (to the extent that the records can be trusted) represent variations of about 15 per cent, about the present-day means for temperature at various latitudes, these being in all cases relative to the freezing point of water, which has an obvious ecological significance. Thus a place with a present-day mean annual temperature of 10°C has perhaps had periods when the mean was as low as 8·5°C. or as high as 11·5°C. Referred to absolute zero, which would be the only logical basis when considering extra-terrestrial causes of temperature change, the variation becomes about $\pm 0{\cdot}3$ per cent. In the case of rainfall, overlapping thirty-year means have been plotted by Lysgaard* for Rome, Milan, Copenhagen, and Edinburgh, starting with 1771–1800 and finishing with 1921–50. The maximum ranges of variation of the thirty-year means about the 150-year mean are approximately 13, 9, 5 and 7 per cent respectively. Annual rainfall totals, on the other hand, during the geologically insignificant period of more or less reliable records, have a range of variation so much greater that their presentation in terms of percentage is misleading. In northern Europe, for instance, variations can be between about 80 per cent or less of the mean (–20 per cent) and about 140 per cent of the mean (+40 per cent). In the Middle East and southern Mediterranean zone, the range of variation can be between about 25 per cent of the mean (–75 per cent) and

* UNESCO Symposium on Climatic Change.

about 250 per cent of the mean (+150 per cent), and along the desert fringe this range can increase to –100 per cent (zero rainfall) and +300 per cent; or an even greater higher limit in extreme cases, accompanied by more frequent occurrence of zero rainfall.

Wherever we choose in the latitudinal belt between the northern edge of the Sahara desert belt and the Arctic, year-to-year rainfall variations can be at least one order of magnitude, and sometimes approach two orders, greater than those of other parameters.

One of the first things that any hydrologist learns, more quickly if he is concerned with arid zones, is that the mean rainfall of a place bears no simple relationship to actual rainfall. The mean, as already explained, is a statistical concept only. The same applies to the median. In dealing with any time series, the median is the item or event that is exceeded as often as it is not achieved, and there is a more rational connection in the case of rainfall events with the probability of recurrence of departures from it. Most rainfall time series are more or less skewed, which means in effect that there is more or less divergence between the mean and the median. This, in low rainfall areas, is partly attributable to the fact that there is no obvious limit to the amplitude of positive variation, whereas negative variation is limited by zero rainfall.

In dealing with the hydrological aspects of ecology, it is sufficient for the present purpose to consider only rainfall as being by far the greatest variable. I am not ignoring the importance of evaporation but recognise rather that it, being dependent on relatively less variable parameters such as temperature, humidity, wind, albedo and vegetation cover, can be considered as relatively constant for any one place under constant conditions of land use. Some of the obvious environmental results of rainfall variation, such as great floods, droughts, and wet summers with bad harvests, are easily identifiable in the historical record because they had as much impact as wars and invasions, pestilence and earthquakes. They are often, particularly in the case of floods, uncritically inferred from archaeological data for the prehistoric period.

But I am wandering from the strictly ecological aspect of rainfall. If rainfall, or availability of water originally delivered to the earth as rain, is the most important ecological factor it must play a large part in determining the climax. That climaxes are, within fairly wide limits, climatically determined in the absence of extraneous factors is not disputed. This is, in fact, at the root of most alleged identifications of post-glacial climatic change. What is often overlooked, or given insufficient weight, is the effect of short-term climatic change, of which we have abundant evidence all around us. Climax vegetation is never, in fact, stable, because it depends on too many variables. Of these, probably the most important, after water, from the botanical point of view are changes in soil acidity, either caused by the vegetation itself (e.g. by humus formation), or by changes in soil drainage brought about by the existence of the vegetation, or in other ways.

Soils apart, the association will be formed by those species that are physically available to contribute seeds or spores and that can maintain themselves in balance with other available species in the competition for soil nutrients, water and light, as mature, self-perpetuating individuals.

Their water comes directly or indirectly from rainfall. Directly, as rainfall absorbed locally into the top-soil; indirectly, as ground-water at varying depths and deriving from rainfall. Ground-water on a hill slope may represent rain that has fallen farther uphill more or less recently. Alongside a river, it represents rain or snow that may have fallen at a distance, created run-off and river-flow and reinfiltrated along the flanks of the river to extents governed by the stage of discharge of the latter; possibly reinforced by infiltrated rainfall from adjacent higher ground. In such circumstances, the reinforcement locally may exceed at certain seasons the tendency to infiltrate from the river, so that a positive gradient towards the latter is established. The river then becomes a drain for surplus ground-water rather than a source of it. In situations such as plains, ground-water may represent the accumulation of water from many sources, near and far, all originally rainfall, with different lapsed times between their occurrence as rainfall and their arrival in (and slow passage through) the aquifer under the plain. In desert, arid, and semi-arid situations, ground-water often represents rain that has fallen at a great distance and nearly always seasonally, and it may be at such a great depth that only in topographically suitable points does its level reach up to or near the surface, creating oases. Even artesian water derives ultimately from rainfall whether it is natural, as in the case of some springs, or appears only as the result of well-drilling. Normal springs are essentially of the same nature as oases for they occur where the ground surface locally is lower than the water-table.

To the extent that the situation of the climax vegetation is dependent on ground-water, and according to the distance at which the rain falls that supplies the ground-water, the mean rainfall (not in this case the median) assumes greater or less importance. In a hypothetical situation dependent entirely on ground-water that has come a very long way in a very long time since its original occurrence as rain, the climax can be entirely dependent on mean rainfall. Something approaching these conditions occurs in desert oases—situations which are only sensitive to relatively long-term rainfall variations. Everywhere else, except in situations that are almost entirely dependent on rainfall such as hill slopes well intersected by natural drainage channels, the water background is very complicated. So complicated that it is impossible to deduce a general rainfall relationship, and difficult to deduce even a particular relationship which will hold good under all circumstances for any one place.

From the point of view of ecology, therefore, there are a very few situations where the mean rainfall, often that of another quite remote place, governs the vegetation entirely through ground-water, and a fairly large proportion of situations where the full variability of local rainfall is the governing factor. In between, all situations reflect these varying combinations of the local rainfall and of ground-water variability.

Of the two extremes, wetness and dryness, of divergence from normal conditions, dryness is of more ecological significance and more determinant of the climax than wetness. As the amount of rainfall increases above a certain point, the proportion that runs off as flood-flows, or infiltrates below the root zone, increases very much more than proportionately, so that the amount of available plant moisture contributed by years of higher than normal rainfall is not very much increased. The actual increase depends on the degree of permeability of the soil, the intensity of the rainfall, the capacity of a permeable soil to store water, the distribution in time of the rain, etc.

In the case of lower than normal rainfall, the effect is generally proportional to the deficit, for low rainfall almost always implies longer periods without rain and, therefore, more loss of what little rain there is through evaporation and transpiration.

Whether periods of higher and lower rainfall are subject to predictable periodicity is mainly a matter of interest for the future. Periodic or not, these variations have occurred throughout time because their causes have always been with us. And so we have to accept the fact that periods of several, sometimes many, consecutive years of drought have occurred as they are occurring today. The result for any given combination of soils, normal rainfall, temperature, drainage, and evaporation, is and was the inhibition of those plant species that are and were not able to tolerate moisture deficiency; not necessarily their destruction, but certainly their relegation to a minor part in the association. The corollary is the domination of those plant species that can tolerate drought. This dominance can be temporarily reversed, particularly for short-lived species, by a series of wet years during which survivors of inhibited species may make a temporary come-back but, as already noted, the additional available moisture in wet conditions is not proportionately greater. The climax vegetation, in short, automatically adjusts itself to all the environmental parameters including that of rainfall variability, and tends to be determined by the incidence of drought.

If periods of relative drought followed a regular pattern, the climax would tend to be stable in respect of climatic factors, while still remaining sensitive to gradual soil changes. It is clear, however, even from short-term modern records, that there is no regularity, and that even the obvious irregularities in the incidence of series of below normal years of rainfall are often supplemented by otherwise normal years in which the effects of low annual totals are simulated by maldistribution of rainfall.

A period of long sustained drought can have as decisive an effect in a situation dependent on rainfall as can a major change in the water-table, whether this last is due to deficient rainfall, to normal geomorphological processes, or to drainage changes occasioned by tectonic action or sea-level changes. In either case, the climax adjusts itself to drier conditions with the dying out of certain species. In these conditions, a sort of chain reaction can be started. For instance, the dying out of deep-rooted species would stop or reduce the process of transferring soil minerals from deep horizons to the surface soil. One consequence would be impoverishment of the top-soil by shallow-rooted vegetation, followed by reduction of the latter and eventual destruction of the soil structure and erosion. When the long sustained drought ends, the process is only reversible at all, and then only slowly, if nearby specimens of the original population have survived in habitat niches from which their seeds can easily and quickly reach the depopulated area. Often the process can be so nearly irreversible as to leave apparent evidence of a major climate change. This is not necessarily a better explanation of climax changes than the hitherto generally accepted one of major climatic changes, but at least it takes account of the basic short-term variability of rainfall of which we have plenty of evidence. I think it would be reasonable to suggest that if major climate changes have taken place, their effects would almost certainly have been ecologically less effective than short-term variations of far greater amplitude: and so any evidence that such changes may have left would be virtually impossible to detect.

Another feature of high short-term rainfall variations is their local nature. A long period of drought in Britain *could* have covered most of the country, but would probably not have had a simultaneous incidence over the whole of France and would almost certainly have had no echo in the Mediterranean or in eastern Europe. This may account for vegetationally defined climate phases that do not agree in their dates.

While the effects in northern Europe of short-term rainfall variations could, from time to time, have produced local changes of ecological associations without any permanent change (for instance, from forest to steppe), the effect in the southern Mediterranean and Near East, with lower and more variable and seasonally defined rainfalls might be expected to be greater. And yet it is precisely from the Near East and Middle East that evidence of biological continuity suggests that the effects of climate change, whether long-term or short-term, have been minimal. As Braidwood* has pointed out, the cultigens found in datable levels at Jarmo and Karim Shahr, etc., on the flanks of the Zagros, still grow around the ancient sites wherever the activities of man and animals have permitted their survival.

These cultigens—barley, pulses, and the like—are almost by definition plants with heavy seeds which can only rarely have been transported uphill, and then rather through the agency of animals than through wind or rain. And yet in times of drought, the normal rainfall of a certain place can only be found by going uphill. Heavy fruiting is a characteristic of xerophytes. Their continued existence in a semi-arid environment points to continuously semi-arid conditions for some 9,000 years. For what would have happened had there intervened, as some would have it, a long, comparatively moist period corresponding to a climatic optimum? The tendency for heavy seeds to be washed downhill and the downhill shift of rainfall normals would have tended to establish these already specialised plants at a lower altitude. This is perfectly logical and so is the fact that other less specialised xerophytes would have tended to move into their original higher habitat from even farther uphill. Better adapted to higher rainfall, the new species would have crowded out the old. What is not logical or comprehensible is how, with the alleged return of drier conditions, all these associations could have returned uphill.

Undoubtedly, limited downhill migrations would have occurred during long dry spells, but it seems evident that the dryness was never so great or so long-sustained as to kill out these species from their present habitat. A partial explanation may possibly be that there was also lateral migration,

* Braidwood *et al.*, 'Prehistoric Investigations in Iraqi Kurdistan', *Studies in Ancient Oriental Civilisations*, Chicago, Vol. 31 (1960).

with little loss of altitude, from dry ridges to limited habitat niches in adjacent drainage lines, but some degree of downward movement and subsequent return uphill would still be necessary. It is, of course, possible that in the alleged return of comparative aridity that followed a climatic optimum, the cultigens were moved uphill by man, but the proposed dates do not encourage this belief. By the time this return to comparative aridity is supposed to have happened—dated by many to the third millennium B.C. or even later—man was surely no longer preoccupied by the original cultigens, having reached a fair degree of experience as an agriculturist with the introduction of different species such as six-row barley. The original wild barley was two-row.

It is frequently asserted, and often with good reasons, that areas now devoid of forest cover were previously more or less densely forested. It is only necessary to go back some fifty years in Jordan for proof of this, for large areas in southern Jordan were most effectively and systematically deforested during the First World War in order to find fuel for the Hejaz railway. This was, of course, nothing to do with climate or rainfall. The process that then, under the stress of war, took only a few years, has been going on for hundreds, even thousands of years. Anyone who has experienced the Jordan winter or learned something of it from Lawrence's *Revolt in the Desert* can hardly be surprised. Timber and scrub are the only sources of fuel that are actually produced within Jordan itself and they are both also a source of browse for Bedu flocks. The miracle is that any forest has survived in southern Jordan, as it has in remote corners near Tafila, Shaubak, and Wadi Musa: it was saved by difficulty of access from the Turkish military authorities during the First World War, and by comparative remoteness from all but very small population centres. The remnants, mainly of scrub oak with a few elderly pistachio, show what the forest association could be without the intervention of man and animals. It would be more correct to speak of the remants of forest as open woodland but in the present context it is of minor importance.

Shaubak, with some 350–400 mm. mean rainfall, is today the site of a forestry nursery, and the shallow plateau valley running south from there towards Hai and Wadi Musa is a fairly flourishing dry-farming area with patches of orchard irrigated from wells.

The desiccation of much of Jordan, however, of which man and animals have been the surprisingly slow agents, would probably have happened sooner or later even without their agency. This is because in arid areas the effects of variability of rainfall and of long periods of drought are slowly and insidiously irreversible.

I have proposed as a working hypothesis that there have been no major world-wide post-glacial climate changes. I will go further and suggest that any changes that there may have been have not been of a magnitude sufficient to cause observed ecological change, assuming for the moment that the evidence for such change has been correctly interpreted. As a corollary it is suggested that ecological changes have been due mainly to the following causes: the built-in year-to-year variability of climate and particularly of rainfall; the intervention of biotic factors such as fire or plant diseases; the intervention of man and animals; changes in drainage caused by geomorphological processes such as change of sea-level, tectonic and volcanic activity, and the erosion, transportation, and deposition of sediments, often themselves originating indirectly from changes in ecology wrought by one or more of the other factors. The only thing new in this is the exclusion of secular world-wide climatic change. This hypothesis only very marginally simplifies the interpretation of prehistoric environment for the remaining factors are quite complicated enough in their actions and interactions. However, some overall simplification is introduced in that we are enabled to use the observations of today without having to make unjustified guesses about the prehistoric climatic background.

PART II

THE EFFECT OF POST-GLACIAL CLIMATE AND WATER RESOURCES ON EARLY HUMAN SOCIETIES

7 THE EVIDENCE FOR POST-GLACIAL CLIMATE CHANGE

The detailed interpretation of the various kinds of evidence for post-glacial climate change can only be made by the appropriate experts, either working alone or preferably in collaboration with those in other fields. It is, however, legitimate for anyone to take an objective look at the evidence itself, the raw data, and check it for internal consistency. It is also legitimate for him to consider the declared limitations of the interpretative methods used in other fields where those limitations have been authoritatively admitted. Where any of the interpretations involve hydrology, and even more so where they are dependent on hydrological assumptions, it is not merely legitimate for a hydrologist to consider them with a critical eye, but even incumbent on him to do so.

I shall certainly be less vulnerable to criticism, and therefore probably more convincing, if I adopt and maintain the attitude of a more or less informed but sceptical layman with a professional interest in only one part of the problem. I do not want either to try to usurp the functions of other specialists, or to belittle their contributions. The quantity of data available is considerable and has already been presented in easily assimilable form by others—particularly by the late Professor F. E. Zeuner in his monumental achievement *Dating the Past.* The principles underlying many of the specialised methods used in interpreting climate changes are all contained either in Zeuner's book or in *Science and Archaeology* in which a symposium approach was adopted by its editor Edward Pyddoke.

Fortunately there is no need to go through all the mass of relevant data, for a simple axiom makes a brief review quite sufficient: the axiom that climate is a world-wide phenomenon admitting no geographical boundaries other than those inherent in itself. It follows that secular change of climate must also be world-wide, though the direction and nature of the change could be different in different places. The axiom is so widely accepted that it can be reasonably taken as starting-point by sceptical layman and specialist alike.

If, therefore, the dates deduced by various workers as marking climatic phases show little, if any, agreement as between one part of the world and another it must be admitted immediately that something has probably gone wrong. If the dates disagree within a comparatively restricted area such as northern Europe it becomes evident that something *has* gone wrong. This does not imply that the process of reasoning used to establish these discordant dates has been wrong but that there has probably been a mistake in arriving at climate change as the explanation of the evidence of greater or less 'wetness'. It implies that some factor or factors, that could have created the same effects as greater or less 'wetness', have been overlooked.

Apart from the axiomatically universal nature of climate and its secular change there is the question of the data themselves and this applies particularly in the case of sea-level changes. The data must be accepted, but unless they are consistent in amount and direction as between one place and another either the dates ascribed to them are wrong or again some factor or factors have been overlooked. For here another axiom must be stated, at the risk of seeming to state the obvious (many axioms are by their nature statements of the obvious). It is that, at any moment in time, the mean level of the oceans is the same everywhere. It could be objected that the existence of ocean currents implies differences of level without which movement would not occur, but such differences, where they exist, are so small as not to invalidate the axiom. Certainly for any layman they can be ignored for it is no accident that the heights of the land and the depths of the oceans are all referred to the common datum, or fixed level, of mean sea-level. There may be some ocean currents that involve movement of water in the same direction at all depths but the great majority are circulatory in nature.

With this background in mind let us have a look first at the actual data and then at the consistency, or lack of it, of the dates of various climate phases. Both the data and the conclusions drawn come from a number of specialised fields which can be conveniently grouped into geomorphology, botany, zoology, and sundry. A look at some of the geomorphological data presented by Zeuner is instructive:

Nilsson estimated—for Sweden and Denmark—that the sea-level was at –50 metres in about 7500 B.C., rising rapidly thereafter to almost present sea-level in about 2000 B.C. A slight recession to –2 or –3 metres was dated by him to around 1000 B.C., followed by a rise to present sea-level.

Schütte, for north-west Germany, estimated that sea-level was –19 metres in about 7800 B.C.

Godwin, for a coastal site near King's Lynn in England, worked out the following succession of beds and corresponding sea-levels in which I have inserted dates, where possible, according to Nilsson's time-scale:

A	Peat, Pollen Zone VII a	6200–3500 B.C.	–7·2 metres
B	Brackish water clay		–3·2 metres
C	Peat		–5·2 metres
D	Blue Clay, Pollen Zone VII b	3500–*c.*1500 B.C.	+0·6 metres
E	(base) Peat,		–1·5 to –3·0
E	(top) Peat, Pollen Zone VII/VIII	*c.*1500–500 B.C.	–3·4 metres
F	Scrobicularia clay,		+0·6 to +1·5
H	Peat, Pollen Zone VIII	*c.* 500 B.C.	–2·1 to –2·4
		A.D. 1965	0·0

The references to pollen zones will assume greater significance later when botanical evidence is considered. From Zeuner's paragraph which precedes the succession quoted above, the following data have been abstracted:

Submerged peat,	Pollen Zone IV	pre 7900 B.C.	–32 to –52 metres
Submerged peat,	Pollen Zone V/VI	about 7500 B.C.	–35 metres

It must be assumed that –32 metres corresponds with 7900 B.C. and –52 metres with an earlier date. Both these samples are from the bed of the North Sea. The reference in the same paragraph to the water-level passing the –6 metres mark during the Atlantic phase, which covered 2,700 years of Nilsson's time scale, is fairly vague but contrasts none the less with the succession observed by Godwin, and quoted by Zeuner, at Walton-on-the-Naze. This gives:

Late Neolithic	(perhaps 2500 B.C.)	–6 metres
Early Bronze	2000 B.C.	+0·6
Iron Age	1000–500 B.C.	+1·5 to +3·0 metres

A drop in level between Early Bronze and Iron Age is inferred in the text.

When some of the dates lie within very wide brackets it is difficult to make meaningful comparisons, but something will emerge from a retabulation of the data.

From various localities around the North Sea and Baltic and under the North Sea we have:

	England/North Sea		Sweden/Denmark	Germany
	Estimated sea-levels in metres below (−) or above (+) present			
Date or Date Interval		*North Sea*		
Pre 7900 B.C.		−52		
7900 B.C.	*King's Lynn*	−32		−19
7500 B.C.	−35	−35	−50	
6200 B.C.	−7·2			
	−3·2			
→ 3500 B.C.	−5·2	*Walton-on-Naze*		
3500 B.C.				
2500 B.C.	+0·6	− 6·0		
2000 B.C.		+ 0·6	0	
→ 1500 B.C.	−1·5 to −3·0			
1500 B.C.	−3·4			
1000 B.C.		+ 1·5	− 2·0 to −3·0	
→ 550 B.C.	+0·6 to +1·5	+ 3·0		
500 B.C.	−2·1 to −2·4			
A.D. 1965	0	0	0	0

The strange oscillations at King's Lynn between 6200 B.C. and 3500 B.C. apparently have no counterpart in Sweden and Denmark. The fall of between 2·1 and 3·6 metres at King's Lynn between 3500 B.C. and 1500 B.C. compares with a rise at Walton-on-the-Naze of 6·6 metres between 2500 and 2000 B.C. In about 1000 B.C. a rise to +1·5 metres in eastern England occurs, while there is a fall to between −2 and −3 metres in Sweden and Denmark. Levels quoted to the nearest decimetre (about four inches) imply, in the circumstances, careful measurements and there is no obvious reason to doubt them.

In these tabulated results the correspondences are very few and it really does seem that exact agreement at any time must be purely coincidental. Even if other data, not quoted by me, support one series of events against all the others, the contradictions I have noted would still have to be explained. Data of this kind, by their very nature, do not contain the sort of random errors that would justify smoothing the transgression and regression curves that would result from plotting all the levels against time. In fact, if this were done the odd out-of-phase oscillations in eastern England and in Sweden and Denmark would disappear, and there would no longer be even the contradictory evidence of those oscillations from which some part of the climate change deductions have been made. C^{14} datings of cores at various depths at Tilbury do not reveal any of the oscillations that have been identified a little way to the north.

All these examples have been drawn from an area that represents about a tenth of one per cent of the earth's surface. The area can be marginally extended and the contradictions greatly increased by considering one other case, this time from the west of England, quoted by Zeuner. Supporting evidence for the east coast series is said to be afforded by investigations in Bideford Bay in North Devon, where a sequence of post-glacial clays containing a peat bed and a mesolithic industry occurs below high-tide level. The implication is that it occurs at about present mean sea-level. It is said that this indicates a similar sequence of events in the west of England and on the Essex coast. This does not seem to follow at all, as it means in effect that a sea-level some 7 metres lower than that of today on the Essex coast is being equated with one approximately the same as that of today in the west, in about 6000 B.C. It may be relevant that, in the case of the King's Lynn site, the rise of sea-level inferred for the period since 500 B.C. is said to be confirmed by evidence that Fenland sea-walls have been built on successively higher levels for 900 years.

As all the levels that have been considered refer only to the relative levels of land and sea at the points considered, such evidence presumably points to a progressive sinking of the east coast of England relative to the sea. This may have been going on for very much longer than 900 years and at varying rates.

Evidence from the Mediterranean may shed more light of the same kind on the problem. Around the Italian coasts the movements are very confusing and in some cases, probably in all, are certainly attributable to tectonic causes. At the Serapis Temple at Pozzuoli, large up and down relative movements have been recorded throughout history. Paestum, now well above sea-level, is said to have been submerged for a time under the sea but the evidence of submersion here is suspect. Farther south, Metaponto, previously on the coast, now stands inland while what are believed to be the ruins of Sybaris, not far away, are not only deep under more recently deposited clay but below sea-level at that. There is certainly no evidence here of general sea-level change in the period (*c.* 700 B.C. to today) for which such changes are deduced around the North Sea.

To sum up, the geomorphological sea-level data are contradictory and certainly do not suggest world-wide synchronous change. It seems, therefore, that they cannot be used for deducing world-wide climate change unless and until the causes of the contradictions have been identified and evaluated.

The second, and perhaps largest and most important, type of evidence interpreted in terms of climate change is botanical, and it was this type that led to the naming and describing of post-glacial climatic phases. Macroscopic evidence, that is actual remains of leaves, wood, fruit, etc., of various species, was found in existing or former bog situations. Changes of species with depth implied that at various times the vegetation associations had been different. This type of evidence was sufficiently wide-spread (but always in Sweden or Denmark) to suggest a genuine time-series and sufficient artifacts and other archaeological evidence were found to give an indication of the time-scale.

Since this original work, more refined studies have been made using palynology or pollen analysis. It is this which is mainly cited nowadays in climate interpretations so let us briefly review its objectives, and limitations. For more detailed information the reader is referred to Professor Dimbleby's very clear exposition of the subject in the section entitled 'Pollen Analysis' of *The Scientist and Archaeology.*

The objectives of palynology are, broadly speaking, the identification of the vegetation association of the time and place being studied, by quantitative analysis of the pollen preserved or partially preserved in datable horizons. From the results the vegetational climax is deduced, and in this way changes in land use can be detected, and climate change is sometimes inferred.

The limitations of palynology are due to various inherent uncertainties. Pollen grains vary in their resistance to decomposition according to the genus concerned, so that under any conditions there is a tendency for the pollen spectrum to become depleted and distorted with age. This means that an old pollen horizon will tend to contain more than its original proportion of resistant types. In conditions unsuitable for pollen preservation the depletion and distortion are of course much more marked. When comparing similar situations, that are known with certainty to have the same environmental history, this disadvantage does not necessarily affect the broad interpretation of the spectra. However, a comparatively short period of locally changed environment in one of many otherwise similar situations could not only falsify the horizon to which the change belonged but also the underlying horizons. This is a limitation of which palynologists are of course well aware.

In general, pollens are best preserved in those situations where aerobic bacterial action is inhibited. These situations include: some alpine soils where bacterial activity is inhibited by cold; acid soils (those with pH = 5·5 or less); water-logged soils; and desert soils. Those most frequently encountered so far have been acid and water-logged soils. Soils with continuous vegetative cover, and particularly forest cover, tend to become more acid as they mature, but when they start from alkaline parent material the process may take a long time and pollen grains deposited before the critical degree of acidity was reached may have disappeared altogether or may show a completely distorted spectrum. Water-logged situations will preserve complete, *for so long as they remain water-logged,* practically all the pollen grains that originated in them or were brought to them on the wind. A comparatively short period of drying out due to altered drainage could introduce an unknown degree of distortion. The survival of pollen grains in desert soils for several thousand years can be regarded as evidence in favour of the persistence of unbroken desert conditions for the whole period.

Pollens are produced in different quantities by different species and they are produced at different seasons of the year. The atmospheric conditions at the time of pollen distribution may either favour or inhibit long-distance transportation. On the whole, species that rely on wind-pollination produce greater quantities of pollen and this must obviously be of such a size and shape that it is easily wind-borne. It is said that the bulk of the airborne pollen sinks to the ground within a mile or two of its source, but in fact this distance must vary enormously and depend very largely on the meteorological conditions at the time of release of the grains. The many hundreds of analyses of peat-preserved pollen from active bogs which show wind-pollinated species that cannot normally live in a bog habitat are proof only that the pollen came from somewhere else. They cannot prove without quite unjustified assumptions that the pollen was generated within a mile or so of the bog, nor the direction from which the pollen came.

In any but the most favoured locations, pollens are apt to become differently stratified through the action of soil fauna, particularly earth-worms. Earthworms are plentiful in alkaline soils, and so relatively are soil bacteria. In England at least, the wide distribution of calcareous parent material—chalk, limestones, and marls—must severely limit the chances of pollen being preserved in its original stratification in the resulting calcareous soils. Pollen which has lain in the soil for many centuries can become so physically altered by breakage, compression, corrosion, and so on, that both identification of species (or genera) and counting of grains may be impossible. Finally, it is always difficult and generally impossible to distinguish between the pollens of various species of the same genus. As the different species frequently occupy different ecological habitats with different requirements of warmth, light, and moisture, major uncertainty as to the climatic environment is a built-in characteristic.

An illustration of one of these limitations, the difficulty of distinguishing between species, is the case of *Carex* species, the sedges. Keble Martin, in his compact illustrated work

The Concise British Flora in Colour, lists seventy-four species of Carex that occur in the British Isles. He also describes very briefly the type of habitat which each prefers, and in many cases notes whether they prefer acid or basic soils. Leaving aside this preference and omitting all the many species whose habitats are gravelly soils, or other well-drained situations, and whose presence in a peat horizon could only be accounted for by wind transport, the habitats of those preferring boggy, marshy, or water-logged situations vary from high mountains in Scotland to coastal situations in southern England. This habitat spectrum covers a wide range of climate in terms of both rainfall and temperature as well as a latitudinal range of some 500 miles. How, then, can one place reliance on the occurrence of Carex pollen as a climate indicator? The answer, that the other pollens associated with Carex are of more importance than the Carex itself, must carry a certain degree of conviction, but these associated pollens themselves represent genera rather than species, with the genera possibly covering fairly wide habitat spectra.

These limitations create serious problems for palynologists and the frequency with which their interpretations are proved right by other independent forms of evidence represents a considerable achievement. Accepting all these major limitations and others to which Dimbleby draws attention, it is beyond reasonable doubt that palynology is here to stay as a useful archaeological tool and one which will undoubtedly improve in precision as its methods are refined. The evidence, however, does not suggest that it is a reliable tool for interpreting climate.

A look at some of this evidence will have to suffice, for to analyse all of it would take years and add little to our thesis. If merely a limited sample shows definite evidence against wide-spread climatic change or even lack of positive evidence for it, extending the analysis can only be of use if random errors of great magnitude have to be accepted: and if such were the case we could probably place little reliance on the method. If, for instance, at point A in eastern England, pollen analysis at a datable horizon shows Pine climax with Birch; and if at point B at about the same altitude and within a few miles, analysis of a horizon of the same date shows mixed Oak forest, then these vegetational associations are not indicators. As two places near together cannot have at one a 'Boreal' and at the other an 'Atlantic' climate, the vegetation difference must be an indicator of some other ecological factor. If Pine, associated with the early part of the Boreal in Sweden, can be shown to occur all through the Boreal, the Atlantic, and other phases, the risk of using Pine as a climatic indicator becomes obvious.

As these climatic phases are central to this discussion they must be briefly described. The dates ascribed to the various climate phases seem to be generally agreed but the numbering of pollen zones varies from country to country.

In what follows, the Pre-boreal does not really concern us here because its end marks the beginning of the period that concerns this book.

The Pre-boreal is dated pre 7900 B.C. and corresponds with Pollen Zone IV.

The Boreal is dated from *c.* 7900 B.C. to *c.* 6200 B.C. It comprises pollen zones V, VIa, VIb, VIc of the English system.

The Atlantic is dated from *c.* 6200 B.C. to *c.* 3500 B.C. and comprises pollen zone VIIa.

The Sub-boreal, comprising pollen zone VIIb and a transition zone from VII to VIII, is dated from *c.* 3500 B.C. to *c.* 500 B.C.

The Sub-atlantic comprises pollen zones from VIII upwards and extends from *c.* 500 B.C. to the present.

The pollen zones in terms of the dominant tree species are described for eastern England, where many pollen analyses have been carried out, as follows:

Pollen Zone IV represents Birch-Pine climax with Birch predominant. Small quantities of pollen of warmth-loving trees are found while Willow is quite common and non-tree pollen is present in large quantities.

Pollen Zone V is dominated by Pine and the pollen of warmth-loving trees is practically absent. Birch is present in some quantity and Hazel increases at the end of this phase.

;. Transhumance (1) Cattle-owning Arabs of one of the Baggara tribes ı the Western Sudan moving northwards to seasonal grazing and rain-filled ›onds in Central Darfur during the summer rains.

'. Transhumance (2) Camel-owning Arabs of the Western Sudan noving northwards into drier areas at the onset of the summer rains.

8. Transhumance (3) Semi-nomadic Brahui tribespeople from the Jhalawa area of Baluchistan moving down to the warmth of the plains in winter.

9. Transhumance (4) Baluchis moving back into the Sarawan area of Baluchistan from the plains in the early spring. The group shown is on the pass leading to the Isplinji tract.

Pollen Zone VI is a Pine-Hazel climax. Oak and Elm increase and Hazel decreases during this phase.
Pollen Zone VII is dominated by Oak and Alder but contains Elm and Lime.
Pollen Zone VIII is described as an Alder, Oak, Elm, Birch, Beech zone. Birch increases at the expense of the mixed oak forest, and to quote Zeuner's words: 'It is not until this period that the beech becomes a little more prominent in England.'

Undoubtedly Zeuner's descriptions from which the above were condensed were intentionally much simplified. The reference to beech implies that it had appeared earlier, and from diagrams elsewhere in his book it seems that it appeared during VIIb which is distinguished from the earlier VIIa by a decrease in elm. From some time during Zone VII, and particularly in Zone VIIb, Neolithic man was beginning to have an effect through agriculture and so from this time onwards no change can be attributed solely to environmental causes.

All the original work on pollen analysis, and much of the more recent, has been carried out on samples from bog situations, where much of the preserved tree pollen must by definition be exotic. The subsequent fate of the trapped pollen must have depended entirely on the history of the bog itself.

Analysis of some results published recently in *Radio Carbon** produced some results that are difficult to reconcile with the dates of climatic phases or the sequence of changes of vegetational association. A site in Scotland, for example, gives dates of 3700 B.C., 3270 B.C., and 1950 B.C. for VIIa which has been described as extending from 6200 B.C. to 3500 B.C. One sample falls just within this ample time spread, one just outside, and the third misses it by more than 1,500 years. The three samples show Pine beginning in the earliest, at a maximum in the second only 500 years later, and decreasing in the third. Birch is present in the earliest sample, absent from the two later ones but reappears in another, to which no pollen zone is attributed, dated to 1740 B.C.

From another Scottish site the beginning of pollen Zone IV is dated to 6700 B.C. and its end to 5785 B.C., 2,000 years later

* Vol. 7 (1965).

than the generally accepted date. A sample described as late pollen Zone VI is dated to 3525 B.C. According to the accepted climatic-pollen time scale Zone IV ended in 7900 B.C. and late Zone VI would be about 6200 B.C. The ascription of the samples to pollen Zone IV is presumably on account of the dominance of Birch, but taking these two Scottish localities together obviously Birch is not a reliable indicator. These Scottish sites could not be expected to show the same vegetation associations, at any moment in time, as the East Anglian sites but should logically show contemporaneous changes if such changes were due to climatic causes.

Samples from localities in Scandinavia are equally difficult to reconcile. From Finland samples are dated and described as: 7810 and 6440 B.C., lower Birch; 7650 B.C., upper Birch; 8850 B.C., lower part of Birch; 9540 and 5570 B.C., upper part of Birch; and 2800 B.C., with Birch dominant over Pine and Alder, as 'should belong to Atlantic'. The sites from which the samples were obtained are all along the same latitude and within a 33-metre range of altitude: so considering the area rather than individual sites, Birch has been dominant at one time or another (perhaps continuously) for 6,000 years. Other examples from Finland draw a distinction between an 'older Birch' with dates from 7000 B.C. to 5940 B.C. and a 'younger Birch' whose beginning is dated to 2150 and 1170 B.C. at two different sites. These examples are from about 250 kilometres farther north than the preceding ones and from undisclosed altitudes.

Examples from south-central Sweden give a time bracket of 1,000 years for Birch culminating in the climatic optimum dated to 3715 B.C. Elsewhere in Scandinavia and in England Birch is associated with the unquestionably cold conditions of the Pre-boreal, while here it is associated with a maximum of warmth more than 4,000 years later.

A series of thirty-three *Pinus* datings from Sweden gives a time range from 6350 B.C. to 2300 B.C. All samples came from within a latitude range of about 250 kilometres and an altitude range of 600 to 950 metres. The average time gap between samples is 130 years and the longest gap 400 years, so what must have been a random sample gives a remarkably even time distribution. This series of datings does not imply anything about the position of Pine in the vegetational association but does show that it was growing during the whole of a period that, in Sweden, covers the end of the Boreal, the whole of the Atlantic and more than half the Sub-boreal.

Many other examples of discordance could be quoted but these should be sufficient to give food for thought. The definition of pollen zones according to the species contained seems to have little dating relevance except locally. It seems too that there is no consistent correlation, even within small areas, between pollen zones and their dates. It follows, therefore, from the original axiom (that secular climate changes must be world-wide) that some factor other than climate fluctuations must account for the changes of pollen spectrums.

The evidence considered so far has all come from fairly high northern latitudes. But palynology has been widely used over most parts of the world. I will take my last example from a very different type of environment, that of the Hoggar and Tibesti mountains in the Sahara. The Saharan environment is not only climatically very different but also not particularly favourable for the preservation of pollen.

Pollen analyses from these mountain oases of the Sahara are said to indicate a period of relatively high rainfall, resulting in a flourishing Mediterranean flora, some 4,000 to 5,000 years ago. Now, so far as I know, it has never been claimed that pollen analysis can indicate the density of vegetation and I am sure that it could never do so. Under satisfactory conditions for preservation of the grains it can indicate that certain genera existed and, with very careful interpretation, it can indicate the proportions in which they were associated. Whether or not the climate at that time was more rainy than that of today, it can hardly be doubted that the conditions since then have been extremely unfavourable for the preservation of pollen. Very little reliable information is available, but the existence of small surviving areas of Mediterranean-type flora and of springs indicates a small high-altitude semi-arid climate with consquent seasonal fluctuations in soil moisture and, almost certainly, highly variable rainfall. In the areas where vegetation survives because of sufficient soil moisture the conditions for preservation of pollen are not desert conditions and they are certainly not waterlogged. The pollen spectrum could therefore be expected to be considerably distorted with age, and the possibility must be considered that 5,000 years represents the limit of survival of a fairly representative spectrum. It cannot therefore be assumed that pre 3000 B.C. the conditions were wetter. There is no reason to doubt that from about that time onwards the vegetation became gradually more sparse until the denuded conditions of today were reached, but there is at least one feasible explanation of this that does not require the postulation of climate change. I will come to this in the next chapter.

I think it must be admitted that the evidence of palynology is too contradictory to make its use as a climatic indicator convincing; and that some non-climatic factor or factors must have been overlooked. A partial and local exception can perhaps be made in the case of the pollen evidence for an 'Atlantic' phase about which more will be said later. However, even if palynology fails to convince as a climate indicator, it remains an invaluable archaeological tool for the identification of man's prehistoric floral environment, and I believe that it will become an even better and more precise one as soon as it is released from the subjectivity implicit in acceptance of climatic phases.

An up and coming botanical tool of a quite different kind is dendrochronology. As it has not yet been used to interpret anything beyond local and comparatively short-term climate fluctuations I will not say anything about it except to appeal to its users to be very careful how they deduce anything beyond soil moisture conditions and temperature fluctuations from it. I have already seen one report in which it was claimed that rainfall and run-off variation could be deduced from analysis of tree-rings. Any such claim reveals a frightening failure to appreciate the basic principles of hydrology and an inexcusable readiness to use technical terms, such as 'run-off', that could convey the misleading impression that the principles are understood.

In considering the zoological evidence that has been adduced as indicating post-glacial climate changes it is essential to remember two things. The first is that the mobility of many animals is such that they are able to take advantage, through transhumance, of seasonal variations of temperature and rainfall and also, perhaps more importantly, escape the worst consequences of local droughts: drought mainly affects herbivores, and transhumance in the animal world is essentially their response to vegetational and other factors directly dependent on climate, but carnivores follow the movements of their herbivorous prey. The second is that animals are extraordinarily adaptable to differences of climate and, even within the habitat of individuals, can tolerate extremes that are not always obvious to human observers. I know even less about zoology than I do about botany. I do not know the precise chain of cause and effect that leads to animal transhumance but I know that it occurs in such varied places as the southern edge of the Sahara, the mountains and plains of Baluchistan, the northern edge of the desert belt in Jordan, and in East Africa. I do not know how the mechanism of adaptability to climate functions in an animal but I know, for instance, that camels are obviously better adapted to extremes of heat and cold than I am.

The first example that I want to look at with a sceptical layman's eye concerns camels. Camel bones in Alaska dated *c* 4000 B.C. are said to indicate warmer conditions at that time. (Lamb: proc. UNESCO/WMO Conference, 1961, p. 126.) But this sort of reasoning is, on the face of it, so absurd that it is difficult to take it seriously. Are we to infer that for a period of perhaps a thousand years or so around 4000 B.C., and only then, camels were to be found in Alaska? If they were already there in the preceding colder period their existence in the allegedly warmer period is not in itself an argument for its being warmer. And if not, where did they come from? The map of North America does not indicate easy migration routes from the South and in any case the latitude differences required to compensate for the earlier cold cannot have been very great. The explanation is probably much more simple and nothing to do with secular climate change. All the camels are said to have originated in North America,* and presumably must have inhabited Alaska, if only in transit, in order to spread into Eurasia. That they inhabited it during its coldest period is surely clear from the fact that they could only have

* Zeuner, in *A History of Domesticated Animals.*

migrated across the Bering Straits when these were either ice-bound or, possibly, dry land owing to glacial eustasy/isostasy. So, clearly at one stage in its history, the ancestor or ancestors of the Dromedary and Bactrian were either adapted to or tolerant of great cold: the Bactrian is still so adapted. The disappearance of camels from Alaska during the Holocene could be due to many causes.

The association of camels with heat is understandable but surely wrong. Their adaptation is in fact to lack of water and seasonal availability of food. In the plateau area of Baluchistan around Quetta at an altitude of some 1,700 metres, the winters can be exceedingly cold. The combination of occasional clear winter skies, of altitude, of drainage of colder air from the 3,000-metre mountains that surround the high plateau valleys, and incursions of cold air from the North, can result in winter temperatures of –20°C. Yet camels are used there winter and summer and appear to exhibit distress only when trying to negotiate slippery snow-covered roads. In the southern Libyan desert during the winter *gizzu* migration, hundreds of thousands of camels of the Arab Kawahla and Kababish tribes and of the Meidobi and Zaghawi spend three or four months in very cold conditions. Night temperatures drop to –10°C. on occasion and there is generally only a brief period in the afternoon when the sun's heat overcomes the piercing cold.

The next example concerns me both as sceptical layman and as hydrologist. In much that has been written about the Indus civilisation it has been inferred, partly from the faunal species depicted on seals and pottery, that the Indus valley, about 4,000 years ago, enjoyed a wetter climate. The Indus people decorated their pottery mainly with bulls and floral motifs, but their exquisitely carved tablet seals of steatite depict a fairly wide range of wild and domesticated animals. Bulls, rhinoceros, elephants are common subjects, and the occurrence of rhinoceros, in particular, has been adduced as evidence of wetter conditions than those of today. Moreover, it is claimed that this demonstrates wetter conditions at Mohenjo-daro itself, where such seals have been found during excavations. The somewhat uncritical acceptance of faunal and other evidence has caused much misunderstanding of the

Indus environment. The late Sir Aurel Stein, writing about forty years ago, asserted that desiccation of the climate of Pakistan and Baluchistan had occurred since Indus Civilisation times and was probably continuing. It is not only faunal evidence that was cited by Stein, and since quoted by others, but for the moment let us consider the faunal evidence in isolation.

The Indus Civilisation covered a vast area that included the whole valley of the Indus itself and those of its main tributaries in the Punjab, as far as the foothills of the Himalaya. It extended eastward into Rajasthan and to Delhi (if not farther), and south-eastward to the Gulf of Cambay; and it had trading establishments along the Arabian Sea coast at least as far west as the modern boundary between Pakistan and Iran. In addition it had relationships, evidenced by the discovery of Indus-type ceramics, with many of the chalcolithic cultures of Baluchistan, and with Sumeria. Whether the Baluchistan contacts were trading relationships or more in the nature of colonial overlordship remains to be determined. Within this vast area there is a great variety of climate, topography and, even today, of jungle habitat where all the fauna depicted on the seals could exist if man had not virtually exterminated it. The existence in a London surburban sitting room of Landseer's 'Stag at Bay' does not mean that red deer roamed London in the nineteenth century.

One further example of faunal evidence must suffice. In the western Sahara mammalian bones, of species that could not possibly survive the conditions of today, have been fairly confidently dated to about 4000 B.C. and a change of climate since that time has been inferred with some confidence.* The species include elephant and it is relevant to note that these still survived in the Atlas until early historic times. They also include hippopotamus. In tracing the history of the western Sahara, McBurney himself supplies a possible explanation that is independent of climate. It seems that before about 4000 B.C. the upper Niger, which now flows through a swamp area not far from Timbuctoo to join the lower Niger, flowed northwards into the Sahara into the depression known as El Juf. Its fossil course is said to be clearly revealed in air

* McBurney in *The Stone Age of North Africa.*

photographs. The consequences of this, and a different interpretation, will be examined in the next chapter.

Two examples of the kind of evidence that I described as 'sundry' must suffice for this review. The first concerns the Caspian. Evidence of a continuous, if irregular, fall in the level of the Caspian Sea has been cited as indicating progressive desiccation of the surrounding area. This interpretation, whether from the common sense point of view or that of hydrology, is quite unjustified. The Caspian derives its water overwhelmingly from the Volga and its level depends on precipitation and run-off far to the north between latitudes 45° and 60° N. and on the amount evaporated from the sea itself. It is hardly dependent at all on its immediate surroundings.

The second example concerns recent work done on the ratio of the oxygen isotopes O^{16} and O^{18} in the remains of foraminifera compared with the ratio in sea-water today under varying temperature conditions. From exact analyses of the ratio the temperature of the sea, at the time when the foraminifera lived, can be deduced. I am not at all familiar with the method or with the principles on which it is based and so have to accept unhesitatingly that the calculated sea temperatures are right. However, I cannot go beyond this and accept that the estimated sea temperature at a certain place at a certain time in the post-glacial period is necessarily evidence of the climate at that place and time. For, without knowing anything about oxygen isotopes, it is obvious that sea temperatures are the result of a complicated process of absorption of heat (from the air or sun), its movement by convection currents and drift currents, and the giving up of heat somewhere else (to the air or in ice formation). The temperature of the water at place A and in the year X B.C. probably had nothing to do with the climate at A at that time and much to do with the bringing in of warm or cool water from elsewhere by drift currents. Such currents today follow a fairly invariable course with at most seasonal variations but, when the sea-level was some 60 to 100 metres lower, the whole circulatory system must have been entirely different. It is only necessary to consider the closing of the Bering Straits and the English Channel to appreciate this. Apart from that, a lower sea-level would have involved an entirely different (and probably much decreased) distribution of shallow water areas over continental shelves where the seasonal warming and cooling would have been quite different from that of today.

To sum up this review of the evidence for post-glacial secular climate change it seems to me that the best verdict it can hope for is 'not proven'. The data are contradictory; some of the methods employed fail to convince as soon as they are stretched in an attempt to yield more information than was ever intended; the deductions pay scant regard to hydrological principles; and their lack of concordance suggests that a factor or factors of importance have been overlooked. In the next chapter I will introduce some new factors and elaborate some of those already introduced. I do not believe that the climate phases with which I disagree are of great intrinsic importance. Their importance lies in the attitude of mind that has permitted their survival for so long and with so little criticism; and this attitude becomes much more serious when it is extended to the solution of specific problems. There is a wide-spread tendency to permit the auto-genesis of error arising out of error, that becomes confused with truth. I selected the climate phases for criticism because they are of comparatively wide interest and fairly universally accepted.

Now I will attempt to suggest other interpretations that fit the few facts of which we have knowledge without violating natural laws.

8 A NEW CLIMATIC HYPOTHESIS

I have referred to factors that seem to have been overlooked by those who have identified, described, and dated the post-glacial climatic phases. Consideration of one of these factors leads to the rather unexpected conclusion that there is good reason to deduce different climatic conditions for one of the phases in a very limited area. The phase is that known as the 'Atlantic', and the limited area is exactly that in which most of the work on climate phases has been done—the North Sea and the areas immediately surrounding it. However, this discovery does not invalidate either the criticism of climatic phases in general or of the accepted interpretation of the Atlantic phase. This factor is not a new one and it has only been overlooked in the sense that its significance has not been fully understood. Each climate phase, as described earlier, is considered as having had, for many hundreds of years at a time, climatic conditions definable in broad terms such as warm dry or warm moist that distinguished it more or less sharply from the phases preceding and succeeding it.

The Atlantic phase in the restricted area described is dated from *c.* 6200 B.C. to *c.* 3500 B.C. From somewhere around 10,000 B.C. to a date that has been estimated as *c.* 4000 B.C. on archaeological grounds, the eustatic-isostatic post-glacial rise in ocean-level was taking place from a glacial low level of perhaps –100 metres to present sea-level. At the beginning of this period, what is now the North Sea was dry land to about 57° North latitude or even rather farther north. Some time during the 6,000 years of marine transgression the effect of this transgression began to make itself felt on the North Sea plain. 6200 B.C. is as likely a time as any other.

When the North Sea plain was dry land the climates of Denmark, north-west Germany, the extreme south of Sweden and, to a lesser extent, the Netherlands and north-east

France would have been marginally more continental than they are now. When present sea-level was reached all these places would have had, as they do now, a relatively more oceanic climate owing to the moderating effect of the North Sea. So the period known as the Atlantic would have represented, for these areas, a gradual transition from more continental to more oceanic climate. It would be quite wrong to describe the whole period as oceanic or to attribute to the whole of it any other steady condition, for it would have been inescapably a period of change. On this reasoning it is logical to describe the preceding phase, the Boreal, as more continental, but quite illogical to postulate a return to continental conditions at the end of it. There may be other parts of the world where, locally, the post-glacial transgression caused a similar transition over the same period.

However, the rise of sea-level would have had a very substantial effect on the coastal drainage patterns everywhere. The steadily rising drainage base-level would have had an enormous effect on ground-water gradients so that areas that had previously been dry and well-drained could have become water-logged and swampy. The gradual establishment of high water tables would have had a much more profound effect on vegetation than slight local changes of climate. The rising base-level due to eustatic rise was accompanied by isostatic tilting of which the effect, in changed drainage gradients, could have been felt over enormous areas inland. The so-called climatic optimum and its occurrence at widely differing periods over a comparatively small area of the world was probably caused by the response at various places to changing drainage régimes and had nothing to do with climate at all.

The recurrence horizons or *Grenzhorizont* found in bogs or former bogs are much more convincingly explicable in terms of drainage changes than by climate change. These horizons are said to indicate differing conditions of moisture and probably did so—but not as a result of more or less rain.

A climatic 'phase' implies that during its existence a certain general type of climate persisted that can be distinguished from those of the periods preceding and following it: and so post-glacial climatic phases are described as follows:

	North America	N.W. Europe
Pre-boreal	Cool	transition to warm and dry
Boreal	warm, dry	warm, dry
Atlantic	warm, moist	humid and mild
Sub-boreal	warm, dry	drier, more continental
Sub-atlantic	cool, wet	cooler, more oceanic.

There seems to be no reason to disagree with the description of the immediately post-glacial Pre-boreal as cool or alternatively as a period of transition to relative warmth. But there seems to be plenty of reason to doubt that the warm, dry Boreal was any warmer or drier than the climate of today except in limited areas. The Atlantic, in those same limited areas where rising sea-level caused local direct changes of climate, was not a phase but a period of gradual transition during which a previously more continental climate became a more oceanic one. From the end of the Atlantic to the present day, the evidence for either universal or local climate change is contradictory whether it be from botany or sea-level oscillations.

Far too little weight is given to the built-in variability of climate that I referred to in Chapter 6. Even if some of the fundamental causes of this variability have been correctly identified in various periodicities of sun-spot occurrence, and others in the persistence of volcanic dust after great eruptions, there remains a great mass of interacting phenomena. These, until all of them are identified and evaluated, must be considered as producing random variations. It is only our ignorance that confers randomness on them. Each phenomenon, in fact, follows as the logical result of the interaction, in obedience to fundamental physical laws, of other phenomena, and in turn becomes one of those interacting factors in giving rise to further change. The effect of chance combinations of climatic conditions may be the result of a kind of resonance effect, among many fundamental causes, making each have a definite periodicity, but I think it is extremely unlikely.

Some of the interdependent factors that create the variability of climate are: the distribution of cloud and the consequent differential direct heating and cooling of the earth's surface; the transfer of warm air to cool areas and of cool air to warmer areas; the presence or absence of sufficient condensation nuclei for cloud formation; the sometimes chance coincidence of high winds and dry powdery surfaces, the depth of accumulation of snow and the time taken for its disappearance; invasions into high latitudes of warm, moist tropical air; outbreaks of cold polar air that sometimes reach the tropics; the persistence of summer anticyclones over land surfaces with resulting 'heat-wave' conditions, and many more.

One could almost say that in England, where the maximum temperature at Christmas can easily range between +14°C. and -2°C., or that of August Bank Holiday between +35°C. and +12°C. over a period of only a few years, almost anything is possible and that extremes are only improbable. For instance, it is not particularly improbable that southern England should enjoy or suffer, according to the point of view, three or four weeks of complete drought and a general deficiency of annual rainfall. It is considerably less probable that the same sort of thing should happen for three successive years or even more, but it is certainly not impossible. The effect of such a series of years would have a considerable ecological effect, particularly in boggy areas, and could be quite sufficient reason for the formation of a *Grenzhorizont.* If this could happen in England, however rarely, the effect of similar extreme combinations in places that already suffer from very much greater year-to-year variations, can be imagined.

The extreme variability of climatic parameters that results from the complex interaction of interdependent factors reaches its greatest range in the case of precipitation. For at least 350 years scientists have been analysing climatological records in a search for reliable periodicities, for obviously the disastrous effects of drought could be mitigated if its future incidence could be foreseen with accuracy. Many such periodicities have been put forward as hypotheses but none has really proved reliable even for local use. The hypotheses range from the purely empirical, based on frequency analysis of records, to those with a rational background based on cycles of sun-spot activity. In recent years there has been a tendency to correlate climatic phenomena with the rate of change of sun-spot appearance rather than with the maxima or minima of sun-spot numbers. Obviously any climate fluctuations that are solely dependent on extra-terrestrial phenomena such as sun-spots must be in step all over the world. For the variations in emission of solar energy must affect all parts of the world simultaneously. This does not mean that every part of the world would simultaneously experience increased or decreased precipitation, but it does mean that the changes from higher to lower precipitation, or vice versa, anywhere in the world should coincide with changes in one direction or the other everywhere else. However, the periodicities of climatic fluctuations are not the same everywhere and those which do show wide-spread agreement are often of quite different amplitudes. This suggests that extra-terrestrial effects are not powerful enough to overcome the modifying and sometimes cancelling or even reversing effects of the complex of interacting terrestrial factors.

The opinion of Sutcliffe in this connection has already been quoted in Chapter 6. In the same chapter illustrations were given of the way in which the range of variation of seasonal rainfall totals increases as the mean annual rainfall decreases. It is against this background—of built-in variability that increases in amplitude with decreasing 'wetness'—that climate-induced changes in ecological associations should be interpreted. I believe that, with the single exception of localised climate changes induced by large-scale eustatic-isostatic marine transgression (such as that of the North Sea), all changes since about 7000 B.C. or even earlier have been local, random, and of short duration.

The importance of periods of below normal precipitation has already been noted. Vegetation may be inhibited from flowering and fruiting by long-sustained rain and cloudiness but it is better able to withstand such conditions than it is to survive extremes of drought at critical periods. This is largely because the effect of sustained rain is limited by the capacity of the soil to retain moisture and this capacity, except in relatively few badly drained situations, is not lethal: whereas drought, by reducing the soil moisture to vanishing point, can destroy. In any situation, therefore, the vegetation association must surely tend to adapt itself to one that can tolerate minimal rainfall conditions. Below a certain mean annual rainfall, that is probably about 500 mm. or a little less, two secondary factors may exert a decisive influence on vegetation. Even in the absence of extraneous influences such as human interference and fire, prolonged drought can result in such serious loss of soil that the vegetational spectrum is changed. Unless the succeeding period is, by pure chance, free of drought for long enough for the laboriously slow process of soil-formation to replace what was lost, the change may be permanent. When certain species of an association have been lost through drought, even without loss of soil, their re-establishment is entirely dependent on a source of population. If no source is available the loss becomes permanent.

It is to an irreversible change of this kind that I am inclined to attribute the disappearance of an earlier Mediterranean flora from the mountain oases of Hoggar and Tibesti in the Sahara. For these mountain masses are surrounded by hundreds of kilometres of full desert in every direction and it is difficult to see how any species could re-establish apart from the few whose seeds are adapted to long-distance transportation by wind. It is easy to visualise a gradual deterioration, from solely climatic causes, from possibly quite dense Mediterranean flora during the last ice-age to the relics of today. The lowest pollen-analysis date for a representative Mediterranean flora, about 2000 B.C., probably represents the time by which elimination of all but a very few xerophytic species had been completed. There is I believe, even now, in years of good rainfall, enough grazing for seasonal visits of pastoral people: in earlier times the visits were probably much more frequent and involved a much larger animal population. Rock paintings and engravings certainly suggest that this was so. If a transhumance pattern had become firmly established before the virtual disappearance of grazing the forces of tradition and inertia would have tended to keep it in existence even when the land could no longer support the migrating animals; in this way the disappearance of grazing would have been accelerated.

I believe that a similar argument can be used to explain, at least partly, the known cases of desert encroachment. But the parallel is not exact, for although a long drought along the desert margin would eliminate all but the very highly adapted desert species, it would only inhibit, without destroying, the potential source of repopulation in adjacent slightly more rainy areas. On the southern margin of the Libyan desert to the east of the Ennedi mountains there are signs of former habitation where now there are only dunes and scattered desert shrubs. The remains take the form of hut foundations in groups near the foot of the mountains where nowadays there are a few seasonal Bedu-type encampments and near where there are wells; while farther out in the desert quern-stones, sherds, and other artifacts are occasionally found on the clay hard pan base over which the dunes move. The Ennedi mountains are in a way a more southerly example of a mountain oasis. In their case their relatively high, but exceedingly variable, rainfall derives from monsoon air currents. Owing to the lack of sources of repopulation their vegetation spectrum is highly distorted, for while it contains various tree species—*zizyphus*, *balaenites* and acacias—associated with 250–300 mm. farther south, it evidently does not contain many of the normal short-grass savanna species. The place of these is partly taken by some highly adapted desert plants but the whole effect, despite relatively high rainfall, is of a desert with unexpectedly flourishing trees along the wadis.

I admit that I am treading on dangerous botanical ground and can only say, in self-defence, that the hydrologist who ventures a botanical opinion is no more blameworthy than the botanist who ventures a hydrological one! So, on the principle that one might as well be hung for a sheep as for a lamb, I will venture, with great diffidence, a suggestion about the climax changes in northern Europe. To a layman studying Zeuner's illustration of the development of forest in eastern England the picture that emerges is fairly simple. It seems that a Birch climax in the period immediately succeeding the retreat of the glaciers was gradually invaded by Pine, Elm, Oak, Lime, Alder, Beech, and Hornbeam in roughly that order. They are all species that are presumably less tolerant of cold than Birch, which none the less continued to thrive (and still does today in many places all over Britain). To a layman their order of arrival would seem to depend more on the available means

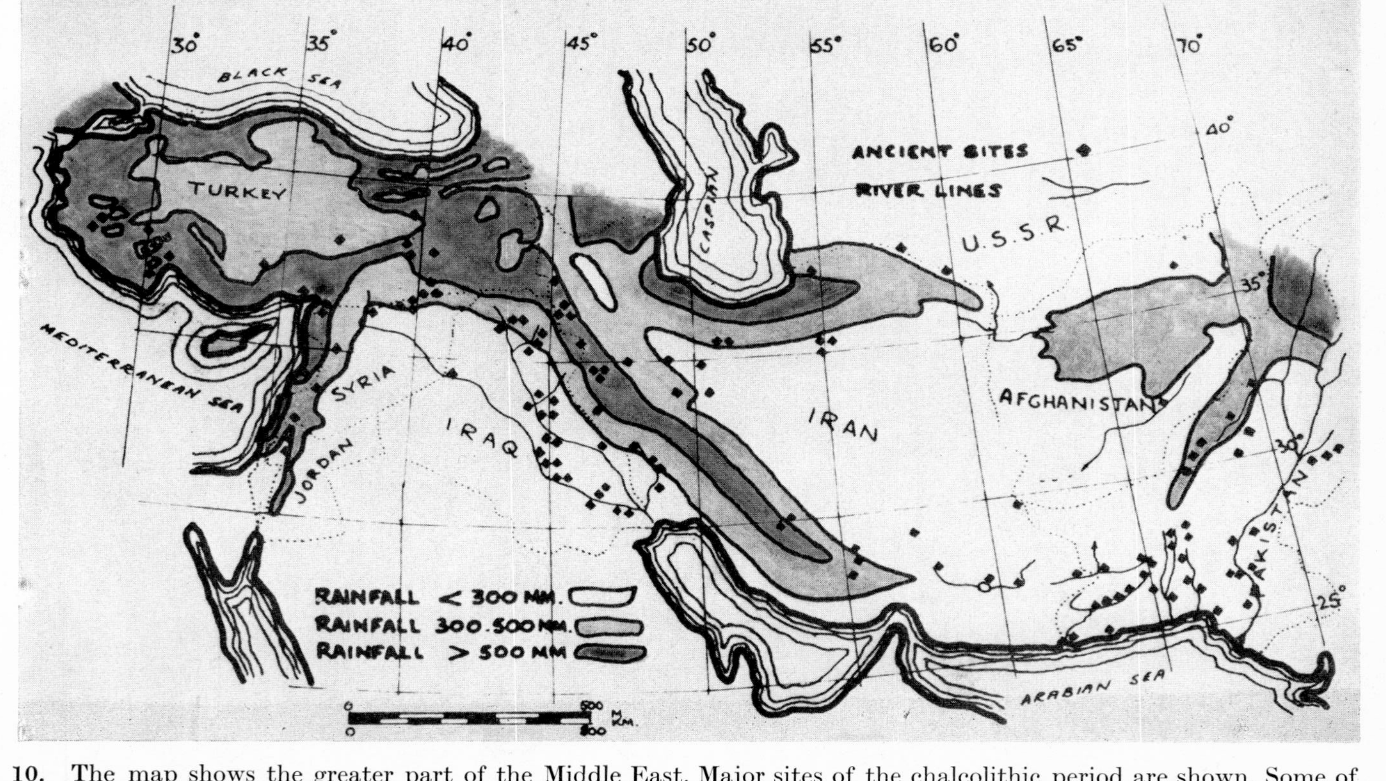

10. The map shows the greater part of the Middle East. Major sites of the chalcolithic period are shown. Some of these sites should perhaps be assigned more precisely to the pottery Neolithic. The period covered is from approximately the mid-sixth millenium B.C. at the earliest to the early second millenium B.C. at the latest. Of particular interest is the evidence of spread into very dry areas along river lines.

11. The corner, abutting on the Hurro Nai (river) in the Ornach Tract, Baluchistan of an exceptionally high *gabarband*. At this point the dry-stone wall formerly turned parallel with the river. In the absence of this corner the structure could have been mistaken for a dam or barrage crossing the river.

12. (*Below*) The same *gabarband* as in 8 seen from slightly upstream and looking generally upstream along the Hurro Nai. The wall of the *gabarband* is invisible because of the accumulated silt whose remains, mixed with some rock debris from the wall and from adjacent slopes, are in the foreground.

of distribution of their seeds than on anything else, once the climate conditions were such as to permit their establishment.

The zoological evidence for a wetter climate in the Indus Valley at the end of the third millennium B.C. has already been discussed and found lacking in conviction. A detailed look at the conditions of today shows that it is not even necessary to rely on the size and diversity of the Indus 'empire' to explain the fauna. At Mohenjo-daro, which was evidently at one time the capital of this empire, the aridity of today can be expressed in terms of a mean annual rainfall of about 75 mm. At Harappa, another closely similar capital farther north, the mean annual rainfall of today is about 125 mm. It is irrelevant to the present argument whether these were simultaneous or successive capitals and, if the latter, which came first. Both cities by virtue of their riverine situations, on the Indus and the tributary Ravi respectively, were in flood-plain environments where rainfall was of minimal importance and the same applied to all the known sites in the complex of the Indus Valley. All of them could have survived and prospered on zero rainfall with or without artificial irrigation, for the Indus complex of rivers enjoys a well-marked seasonal flood that would have inundated vast areas of the flood-plain. Indeed, it would still do so today were it not for the great irrigation barrages of the last 100 years. These harness the annual flood and direct it where it is needed, and a system of artificial flood levées stops the lateral spread of surplus flood water. Even with this system of control, the largest of its kind in the world, uncontrolled flooding still occurs.

The material of the flood-plain is silt and, in much of Sind, silty clay. Both are highly retentive of moisture and the annually inundated areas could have supported (as they do locally today) gallery forest of tamarisk, *Acacia arabica* (*Babul*) and other trees, interspersed with a dense growth of tall grasses. Clearings in this would have afforded the opportunity of growing crops on the receding flood as is still practised today along much of the Nile. From the faunal point of view the enormous flood plains, with an inevitably shallow water table and annual inundation, could have provided a typical jungle habitat affording shelter for elephant, tiger, wild ungulates (including rhinoceros), and a host of others.

If some cataclysmic disaster were to wipe out suddenly all man's environment controls—the barrages, canals and levées—this kind of jungle would rapidly re-establish itself and, provided that a source of faunal repopulation were available, all the typical jungle fauna could be found. But even if this argument were wrong, or if the prehistoric flood régime had been sufficient only to maintain a narrow strip of gallery forest in desert areas, the whole of the vast Punjab area, the extension to Delhi in the Ganges-Jumna valley, and the settlements near the Gulf of Cambay, would have enjoyed at least the fairly considerable monsoon rainfall that they enjoy today. And in the Himalayan foothills all the Indus fauna certainly existed in a wild state until recent historic times. At the other extreme, in Baluchistan, the outposts of the empire would have been familiar with the arid zone fauna—wild sheep and goats, gazelle, possibly domesticated camels, asses and horses, as well as the bears and wolves that are still occasionally found there.

The almost complete disappearance of the wild Baluchistan fauna does not have to rely on climate change as a cause, although gradual degradation of the vegetation caused by high variability of rainfall may well have contributed. Wood and scrub are the only natural fuels, apart from sporadic occurrences of low quality coal in certain localities near Quetta. The Baluchistan winter is bitterly cold: in both winter and summer there is need for fuel for cooking. What the inhabitants, in the course of thousands of years, have not cut for firewood, their flocks of sheep and goats have browsed so that now very few relics of forest survive. The disappearance of cover and the inhabitants' remarkable ability as hunters—armed with beautiful and unexpectedly effective muzzle loaders, using ball-bearings or anything else that comes to hand as ammunition—have led to the near extinction of game. This has had nothing to do with change of climate, though it may possibly be an inevitable consequence of the type of climate experienced for millennia. The point that has escaped the proponents of climate change is that the present climate, of much of Baluchistan and of the Indus Valley, could support a plentiful fauna if man had not destroyed both its vegetation habitat and the fauna itself.

Reference was made earlier to archaeological evidence cited by McBurney and others as indicating a rainy period around 4000 B.C. in the western Sahara. The built-in variability of climate makes it dangerous to reject the evidence absolutely, but there is no evidence to suggest a secular period of high rainfall: and there is a simpler common sense explanation that satisfies the facts.

The ancient Niger, originating in the tropical seasonal rainfall belt, was presumably perennial though variable in discharge as it is now. The evidence of a prehistoric perennial lake in El Juf suggests that perennial flow was maintained throughout the Niger's passage through the desert. Its course must inevitably have been marked by gallery forest and its terminal lake by at least seasonal vegetation, and all along its course and at the terminal lake there would have been water to drink, so that a faunal corridor existed. The archaeological evidence does not suggest that a corridor existed right through to the Atlas, or to the Hoggar to the east, in 4000 B.C.: but it seems reasonable to infer that such extensions did exist during a period of relatively high rainfall such as may have occurred during the last glaciation. It is probably to the last ice-age, therefore, that one must attribute the elephant that were still in the Atlas until Hannibal's time. Rivers, perennial or ephemeral, are not in the least uncommon in the desert. The Nile, Tigris, Euphrates, and Indus are large perennial examples, while some of the streams of southern Jordan are very small ones. They all have one thing in common—that they derive their water from outside the desert.

The case of the Caspian sea-level changes is another example of the kind of evidence that has been used in support of a hypothesis of climate change. It is worth examining in some detail as an example of how hydrology can offer a simple alternative hypothesis. A look at the map will soon convince anyone that a climatic explanation would be improbable, to say the least of it. By far the greatest part of the water reaching the Caspian is contributed by the Volga, which drains a vast fan-shaped catchment area extending from Moscow to the Urals, with its northern limit roughly following the 60th Parallel. The rivers from the Caucasus and the Elburz range of northern Iran can almost be ignored in comparison. There seems no obvious reason to doubt the existence of changes in Caspian level, but there is every reason for relating them to events that happened far to the north, between latitudes 45° and 60°N. The present Caspian level would, in the absence of human control over the Volga, be very sensitive to variation in annual rainfall because a quite considerable rise of level would create a comparatively small increase of the evaporation surface. The level at any time is the result of the momentary equilibrium of inflow and evaporation. Under such sensitive conditions, a rise due to a few successive years of high inflow would take a long time to dissipate, and a drop resulting from a few successive years of drought would also take a long time to recover. The sort of evidence on which early historic Caspian levels are based is too scanty, apart from doubts of its accuracy, to ensure that we are not looking at a totally unrepresentative sample. The consistent recent drop in level is most probably due to the introduction of large-scale irrigation schemes along the lower Volga, while anomalies may be explicable either in terms of short-term rainfall variation in the north, or the development of link canals between the Volga and northward flowing rivers. For prehistoric times, the evidence admits of an explanation owing nothing to climate change. The eustatic rise of ocean levels indicates on archaeological grounds that the period of ice melt probably extended to as late as 4000 B.C. During the previous 4,000–6,000 years, the Caspian shared in the process, with the big difference that it was not part of the vast ocean storage. It must have received from its enormous catchment area an amount of ice-melt entirely disproportionate to its area, and it must have risen from some unknown glacial low point through considerably more than the ocean eustatic rise. The disproportion results from the fact that the ratio of the area of the Caspian Sea to that of the land draining into it is about 1:4·5, whereas the ratio of sea to land areas for the world in general is about 4:1. In the context of glaciations, the Volga drained the south-eastern quadrant of the Fennoscandian ice-cap and although the extent of this, influenced as it was by isostasy, cannot be estimated it must have been very great. In the context of today, this disproportion illustrates vividly the continental nature of the catchment with its very low precipitation. It is not by any means impossible that at some stage during its isolated eustatic rise, the enforced acceptance by the Caspian of a disproportionately high amount of ice-melt could have brought its level to a point where flow to the Black Sea became possible. But none of this implies post-glacial climate change.

Much of the argument so far has been directed against the generally held views about post-glacial climate changes and to reinterpreting the evidence. It is obviously easier to find and interpret (and now reinterpret) positive evidence of change than to demonstrate conclusively the non-existence of change. For this implies at most, in the absence of extraneous factors, gradual adaptation to constant conditions, and by its nature makes unlikely the existence of obvious evidence. However, there is some evidence that directly supports the no-change hypothesis. Probably the most impressive comes from the western slopes of the Zagros from the sites of Jarmo and Karim Shahr in Iraq. Here, and at neighbouring sites, Robert J. Braidwood and others have carried out work of incalculable importance to the study of prehistoric environments. The reference to 'others' should not be allowed to hide the work that Hans Helbaek accomplished in identifying the grains and fruit of cultigens without which much of the relevance of the evidence would be lost. Braidwood contributed to the Climate Change Symposium in Rome and the following information is abstracted from his paper. His conclusions are very much the same as mine. Land-snails, wheat and barley, all of species that are still found wild in the surrounding area, were found in levels dated to 6750 B.C. Wheat and barley which have heavy seeds could easily migrate downhill, during a period of increased rainfall, to a level where the annual rainfall was within their range of tolerance (about 300 to 500 mm. mean annual rainfall with optimum conditions, soil and other factors apart, at about 400 mm.). For with increase of rainfall the isohyets move downhill. It is difficult to see how the same heavy grains could move back uphill against gravity and run-off when rainfall conditions returned to normal, and it seems therefore that any secular change of rainfall that has occurred since 6750 B.C. must have been very small indeed. The evidence of wheat and barley is supported by that of traces of grasses and trees that are essentially of species still inhabiting the adjacent ridges.

At Beidha, where Diana Helbaek (formerly Kirkbride) has been excavating for several seasons with the help of her husband, Hans Helbaek, I had the great pleasure of doing an environmental study for her. Enormous masses of valley-fill have been removed by water since the abandonment of the Neolithic site in the first part of the seventh millennium. An admittedly rough calculation of the volume removed showed that it is consistent with present estimates of flood discharges and their sediment load. In other words, it is not necessary to postulate higher rainfall to account for the removal of valley-fill. The process would be continuing today if the Nabataeans had not constructed excellent terraces to halt the process.

To complete this survey of climate I will summarise my conclusions in the form of a hypothesis or series of hypotheses:

1. From at latest 7000 B.C., and possibly earlier, the world-wide climate has been essentially the same as that of today.

2. The climate today at any place is characterised by great variability of all its parameters in what is essentially a random manner. Therefore the climate of the last 9,000 years has probably been similarly characterised and, because of the length of the period involved, has probably contained extreme occurrences that find no echo in contemporary records.*

3. In certain limited areas the marine transgression that finished in about 4000 B.C. may have slightly modified local climates towards more oceanic characteristics.

4. All over the world the same transgression affected coastal drainage régimes, while isostatic adjustments in and near glaciated areas must have changed inland drainage régimes to some extent. Both these factors could have produced locally the symptoms of climate change.

If this hypothesis is accepted it follows that evidence, particularly botanical, of climate changes must be interpreted in terms of either extreme but short-term examples of the built-in variability of rainfall or drainage changes.

The most that I can hope for is that those concerned with interpreting climate change will pay as much attention to these hypotheses as to those hitherto accepted.

* These words were written before the Italian floods of 4 Nov. 1966.

9 THE RELEVANCE OF THE NEW HYPOTHESIS TO ARCHAEOLOGY

If the identification of post-glacial climate phases is relevant to archaeology, the relevance of any contrary hypothesis cannot reasonably be doubted.

In northern Europe climate was presumably one of the factors that encouraged or discouraged migrations of people. The existence, all through the post-glacial period, of oceanic conditions along the western European seaboard in contrast to the continental conditions of the central part of the Eurasian land mass must surely have been one of the reasons for the succession of migrations and invasions from the East.

In the central Eurasian steppe bitterly cold winters, with sometimes disastrously variable precipitation, and very hot comparatively dry summers, must have made the milder conditions of the West seem very enticing. A possible northward move of people from Spain could have had a similar reason, for much of central and eastern Spain is very dry. Major changes of climate towards continental conditions in western Europe would perhaps have removed the incentive to migrate. I am not talking here of the Boreal which was already finished in western Europe before the change from a Mesolithic hunting and food-gathering economy to the beginning of Neolithic farming. Whatever the climate really was, the Boreal must have been a period of adaptation of vegetation and fauna following the disappearance of glacial conditions. I am thinking rather of the Sub-boreal which, if it existed as a long period of significantly different climate, could have affected migration patterns. But I do not believe that it did, nor that the rapid development of farming at that time had anything to do with climate. The introduction of cereals, native to the semi-arid Middle East, could only have been facilitated in western Europe if the climate had been really similar to that of the Middle East, which is out of the question and has never been suggested. I would expect the introduction of cereal production to have started in continental areas of central Europe where available soil moisture in the spring, under the influence of the annual snow-melt and relatively low evaporation, must be roughly the same (despite very low precipitation) as in the Middle East. The process of adapting cereal cultivation to the conditions of western Europe required the development of new farming techniques and particularly the development of efficient tools to deal with luxuriant spring growth of weeds. So I would expect cereal cultivation to reach western Europe only after a considerable delay.

From the moment when cultivation became established anywhere outside its original home in the Middle East, all vegetational associations came under the distorting influence of man who had to clear away the existing forests to create fields. Man directly affected the associations in this way, and indirectly affected them by starting the process of 'mining' good soil and by changing the run-off régime.

The incentive for pastoral people to migrate westward could have been even greater, and their ability to do so must have been much helped by their comparative mobility. On the other hand, pastoral people would probably have stopped short at the point where the east-west transition from steppe to forest reached an open woodland state. It could never have been worth while to clear vast areas of forest simply to create grazing land, so that westward migration of those who herded cattle and sheep probably followed after extensive (and probably wasteful) clearance of forests by the first cultivators. Apart from the general tendency towards milder climate in western Europe, which must have always existed at least relatively, I do not think that climate, changing or unchanging, had much direct influence on migrations. Once the inherent difficulties of cultivation in the North were overcome the colonisation of forest lands would have gone on mainly because of population pressure elsewhere. This must have had its origins partly at least in the fact that the land had been enabled to support an increasing population that needed more space.

In the fertile crescent the stimulus towards more efficient farming and irrigation must have arisen, as we have seen, directly from the need to overcome man's vulnerability to drought. As a result, in the arid plains the diversion of water from perennial rivers was already being undertaken on a large scale, while northern Europe was experiencing the first introduction of cultivation; and in the mountains, methods that served to conserve both soil and water, such as terracing, ensured that even in drought years some return could be expected from the land. Terracing is an almost infallible sign of highly variable rainfall and run-off, and is generally a sign of strictly seasonal run-off but not necessarily of seasonal rainfall. As it was quite evidently stimulated by need for water I think we must accept that the conservation of soil was an unexpected and welcome by-product.

Abandoned terraces are sometimes considered to be evidence of change of climate, but I know of no case where the abandonment cannot be more easily explained in other ways. Some of these are: a succession of drought years that led to temporary abandonment and consequent failure to maintain the terraces and the structures that diverted water to them; subsequent extensive upstream terracing that reduced run-off and starved the downstream systems; aggrading river beds and increased bed-loss of flood water so that a smaller number of floods could reach the diversion structures.

The second is a very frequent cause. When terraces were first constructed they were not only easier to build on relatively flat (and relatively rainless) downstream lands, but they also produced much larger 'fields'. They were, however, still subject to variability of run-off and received practically no rainfall to supplement it. The engineering problems in building terraces on steep upstream slopes were enormously greater, their maintenance more difficult and their size and shape—as long, narrow contour strips—less easy to cultivate. But they would have received more frequent floods because of much reduced bed-losses near the source of the floods, and they would have also received appreciable rainfall: so although both construction of the terraces and cultivation of them involved much more labour their cultivators were less at the mercy of drought.

All cultivation and grazing of flocks and herds in marginal lands has been more or less subject to the one-way effect of variable rainfall on natural vegetation. This would have some effect, possibly very little but an effect none the less, on run-off and this is a factor to bear in mind in all semi-arid and arid situations. Increased run-off could make the maintenance of terraces difficult and more rapid run-off evidently gives less time in which to divert a portion of a flood on to terraces.

This one-way effect is of particular importance in mountain oases such as the Hoggar, where the disappearance of vegetation formerly able to support quite a large animal population may not be due to desiccation of climate but rather to inherent rainfall variability and the lack of a source of re-population. The prehistory of these Saharan mountain oases should be considered in this light, and it should be remembered that even into historic times the vegetation may well have been more varied and plentiful. In such situations and along all desert margins the denuding effect of over-grazing must be considered. This can go on even where no ponds, springs, or wells are available for animals to drink at. For camels, some kinds of sheep and goats, and for all desert fauna, the fresh green herbage that appears after rain provides both food and drink. The uncontrolled grazing of fresh herbage often allows it to be eaten down to the roots before it can flower and seed. Under such circumstances desert margins can and do advance without climate change.

My emphasis has been on precipitation as an indicator of areas where the transition from collecting to sowing could have taken place: and particularly on the mean annual rainfall. The definition of these areas as those lying between the 300 and 500 mm. isohyets is admittedly a generalisation and should be regarded as an initial guide only. Several things make it risky to use the rainfall parameter, if it is known, by itself, for it is at best only an indicator of available soil moisture which depends among other things on the actual soil and on evapo-transpiration. A few examples will suffice to show its limitations.

If we take the latitude range 30° N to 40° N in which most of the fertile crescent lies, there is obviously an overall tendency for the mean temperature to increase from north to south. The tendency would only show if we could study a series of places that were exactly alike in every respect except that of latitude. In practice differences of altitude, of distance from the sea, of soils, rocks and vegetation, mask the latitude effect, but if we can generalise about rainfall limits we can also generalise about this. The effect would not be very great but might be enough to make the rainfall limits 275–475 mm. in the north and 325–525 mm. in the south. More rain on the whole is needed in the south to give a certain ecological effect, than in the north, because of differences in evapo-transpiration.

Within the general rainfall range of 300–500 mm. there will be places with sandy or gravelly soil, or so-called skeletal soils, where the retention of moisture is negligible: there will be others with clayey silt, that can not only absorb a lot of water but can retain it, and on this even very low rainfall would suffice for vegetation. There will be isolated places, often immediately adjacent to impervious rock, where run-off from the rock surface can so increase the soil moisture that the effect of much higher rainfall is simulated over a small area. It must be remembered, however, that if the mean annual rainfall on the rock is very low its occurrence will be very capricious, so that the adjacent areas would still be vulnerable to the high variability of rainfall.

Local rain-shadow effects, too local to be observable through a normally distributed network of rain-gauges, create local zones of aridity, and the reverse effect—of higher precipitation very locally on mountains—creates local moist zones.

If a mountain ridge runs roughly east-west the difference in evapo-transpiration between the north and south slopes can greatly modify the ecological effect of a given rainfall if all other factors such as local run-off, soil, general rainfall distribution, and so on are the same in the two situations. A north-facing slope can be expected to carry denser vegetation in the northern hemisphere.

In spite of all these local factors I think that the 300–500 mm. isohyetal range is wide enough to give a good guide for the moment to potential areas of search. As experience accumulates it may be necessary to modify the limits somewhat. The existence of the local factors makes it advisable for the advice of a competent hydrologist to be sought if possible.

There is an interesting exception to the general rule. Where rainfall is bi-seasonal and derives from different climatic systems such as Mediterranean-type disturbances in winter and monsoon tropical air in summer, several other factors have to be considered. I have already mentioned one favourable factor—the relative immunity to any given degree of annual rainfall deficiency enjoyed by double-rainfall situations. This is invaluable for the survival of perennial species which can take advantage of the occurrence of above-normal seasonal rainfall for the propagation of their seedlings. It has little beneficial effect on annual species, for these have to complete their cycle of germination, growth, and seeding within a single season of rainfall. If they do not do so on the soil moisture derived from the rain, before the succeeding long rainless period withers them, they cannot survive for long except by accident. Generally the summer and winter seasons of rain are marked by very different rainfall characteristics, humidities, and temperature ranges: this must impose further difficulties. For an annual species to survive in such conditions it has to be highly specialised; it also has to be adapted to the low mean rainfall of either season with all its inherent variability. In such conditions the annual element of an association has perforce to be more drought-resistant than the perennial element. This may be one reason why, in much of Baluchistan, perennials predominate.

In very low rainfall situations, whether one is considering single-season rainfall or one season only of a bi-seasonal system, annual species tend to be restricted to those with a highly adapted germination mechanism: one that only responds when rain has created enough soil moisture to ensure full growth. An example of this mechanism is found in the *gizzu* association of the southern edge of the Libyan desert. The various species produce seeds with hard resistant capsules that do not permit water to reach the germ until the quantity and duration of rain has been such as to ensure survival. It is believed that survival is further ensured by the immediate development of a strong tap-root that probes deeply in search of downward migrating water.

Without some such specialised adaptation, the survival of annual species in bi-seasonal rainfall situations is unlikely and I would not therefore expect to find that the ancestors of our cereals and pulses developed in them. Where a bi-seasonal situation is markedly biased in favour of winter rainfall it gives much the same ecological result as if the weaker season did not exist. The whole cycle of germination, growth, and fruiting is completed before the summer rains can affect it, and the highly sporadic and localised nature of summer storms ensures that any damage, due to premature germination, is also localised. For this reason I would not expect to find a suitable habitat of the wild cereals in Saudi Arabia or southern Baluchistan but would expect to find it in suitable locations in the north of Baluchistan and in Afghanistan.

The *gizzu* has been mentioned several times and is of such intrinsic interest that an otherwise irrelevant digression is justifiable. In the northern Sudan it marks a strip of varying width between the full desert of shifting sands and gravel or mud flats and the extreme north of the perennial grasses, which only grow in exceptionally favourable circumstances, created by local run-off and highly retentive soil, from about 75 mm. mean annual rainfall upwards. The *gizzu* strip, whose width may vary from a few kilometres to a few tens of kilometres, contains large areas of rather fine sand that, when I saw it, appeared to be relatively fixed and to contain a fairly high proportion of coarse silt fraction. The patchy occurrence of the *gizzu* vegetation suggests isolated rain storms as the source of water, but one school of thought holds that it is largely nourished by dew: I find this hard to believe. It germinates in the late autumn and persists through the winter until about March. As this is a dry period it is difficult to believe that rainfall is its source of water unless its specialised germination mechanism somehow imposes a delay in its growth. In fact it may germinate at the end of the summer rains but be inhibited by intense heat until November; but a more likely, if cynical, explanation is that the intense heat of September and October have ensured that no competent observer has ever seen its germination. The *gizzu* plants are mostly semi-succulent and contain enough liquid to make it entirely unnecessary for the camels that graze them to drink.

Enormous herds, literally thousands at a time, are taken into the *gizzu* each winter by camel-owning tribes such as the Kababish and Kawahla as well as by the Meidobi and Zaghawi. Only a few men or boys accompany the herds. The she-camels calve at the outset of the season and the men or boys share their milk with the calves and drink nothing else. For food the herdsmen rely on a few sacks of grain carried with them, and on whatever they can shoot or otherwise kill for meat: desert foxes, gazelle, bustard. Some parts of the *gizzu* are more than 300 kilometres from any well and even where there are wells they are not used. The men appear to be adequately fed and the camels become fat on an almost perfect symbiotic association. The sight of thousands of camels slowly advancing, like an army of animated vacuum-cleaners, across the desert is unforgettable: so is the piercing cold that is the background to their four months' stay.

My climate hypothesis was preceded by one of a different nature concerning the formation and subsequent down-cutting of Pleistocene alluvial terraces. This was that both deposition of valley fill and its down-cutting in semi-arid and arid areas were the result of a relatively slight increase in that type of irregular seasonal rainfall that the same areas experience today. This increase, acting on sparsely vegetated soil before a less xerophytic and more protective vegetation could be established, eroded and deposited great depths of valley-fill wherever slopes and drainage base-levels were suitable. As soon as vegetation became adapted and protected the surface, massive erosion and deposition stopped and the consequent absence of fresh uncemented alluvium reduced the rate of bed-losses. As a result, relatively sediment-free flows were able to persist to points where headward cutting could begin. This continued throughout the rest of the relatively pluvial conditions and, in rivers draining glacier-melt during the retreat of glaciers, it went on during the whole period of deglaciation. In many cases the process of down-cutting was helped and accelerated by changes in base-level and slope caused by eustasy-isostasy or tectonic action.

As in the case of climate, this hypothesis is no more and no less relevant to archaeology than the more widely held view that pluvials represented really major increases of rainfall.

Outside semi-arid and arid areas rainfall was always sufficient to provide protection for the soil: in fact the higher the rainfall the greater the protection. It seems reasonable, therefore, in such areas to equate deposition of valley-fill with marine transgression and raised base-level; and to equate down-cutting with regression. I do not believe, however, that the existence in northern Europe of multiple terrace levels, that is former valley floor levels, means that world-wide marine transgressions necessarily reached correspondingly different levels. This would ignore differences of isostasy and epierogenic and tectonic movements.

Terrace formations are of interest mainly to the student of the Palaeolithic period, for whom the artifacts that they contain provide useful cross-dating checks with cave deposits. Apart from putting forward the view that pluvials north of the desert zone do not need to represent much increase over present-day normals in order to account for terraces, I prefer not to go beyond the guesses already made as to how much the increase may have been in practice. The essence of my case for the use of hydrology is that the parameters should be those of today or that reliable factors should be applicable to those of today. It is one thing to suggest a rather different feasible mechanism for terrace formation and quite another to go on to guess all the possible inter-acting climatic parameters. I hope, however, that the process of deposition and down-cutting, and their causes, suggested here may be considered in future Palaeolithic studies.

It is permissible to add that the mere fact of the occupation of caves over many hundreds or thousands of years is not evidence of wet or even of cold conditions in high latitudes. The absence of a pluvial or ice-age did not mean perpetual warmth and dryness: there were still cold winters and much rain, as there are now. Anyone trying to live a Palaeolithic existence today around the Conca di Fucino, near Avezzano in the Apennines, would assuredly take advantage of the caves that were occupied tens of thousands of years ago, for at least eight months of every year.

Some terraces have been formed in the Holocene and there is a tendency to equate the erosion of which they are evidence with recent rainy phases. Most of the examples that I know are in areas where erosive conditions are maximal, and while an effect of higher rainfall could have been to increase erosion temporarily, there seems little convincing evidence of episodic erosion.

The relevance of the Caspian Sea eustasy is direct. There can hardly be any doubt that the Caspian, draining the melting of an enormous peri-glacial and glacial area, must have stood at an enormously higher level immediately after glacial retreat. Assuming that the Belt Cave near its southern shore has not had its absolute level changed by earth movement, and that its deposits do not contain any sterile material such as might be due to a period of submersion, its level may indicate roughly the immediately post-glacial level of the Caspian. From that level it has consistently fallen and may still be falling today, owing to unbalance between inflow and evaporation over and above any fall due to irrigation diversions. The high former level makes it unlikely that any very early Neolithic sites will be found much below the level of the Belt Cave, making due allowance for movement in this tectonically active area. Incidentally the alluvial terraces in rivers draining north from near Mt Demavend to the Caspian show every indication of having been caused by a lowering of drainage base-level. A rather different example from near the Caspian is described in Part III.

An interesting aspect of post-glacial eustatic rise of sea-level is that of coastal communications. Its importance is recognised in relation to the former land bridges that connected England to continental Europe and the one which probably closed the Bering Straits. Of possibly equal importance in tracing cultural connections are the millions of miles of former coasts now covered by the sea. Coasts and narrow seas have been communication routes since very early times indeed. At the beginning of the post-glacial, communications in the eastern Mediterranean could have involved narrower sea crossings; and extensive tracts of now drowned coastal plains around Italy could have helped the movement of migrant people. The Bosphorus and Sea of Marmora are worth a study in themselves because the Black Sea, during glacial melt, received an entirely disproportionate amount from its enormous catchment. It is inconceivable that there was a land bridge where the Bosphorus now is at any time during eustatic rise, for the outflow from the Black Sea would have been too great.

Some studies of particular cases are described in detail later. Here I will only touch on some of the basic ways in which hydrology can help.

I have already described the process of sedimentation and the conditions under which it occurs. If an ancient site shows evidence of deep waterlaid deposits with a composition similar to that of the flood silt-load of its neighbouring river, it is fairly certain that the deposits occurred under still water conditions. The depth of water required to deposit a certain depth of clayey material depends on the average quantity of sediment transported as a proportion of the volume of flood water: it depends too on the conditions under which the water was impounded and the amount of losses by infiltration and evaporation in relation to inflow. Evaporation losses are dependent on the surface area, and therefore the wider and shallower the flooding the more the evaporation. Infiltration depends in the same way on the area available as well as on the nature of the bed and of whatever is impeding flow.

As a general rule deposits of sediments by flowing water are thin and only occur during the receding stages of a flood when decreasing depth progressively decreases velocity; of course, considerable local thicknesses can build up in hollows. As a general rule the explanation of deep water-laid deposits containing clay has to be sought among such phenomena as landslides, earth uplift or subsidence, or tilting of the earth so as to flatten or reverse a river gradient.

A large amount of varied evidence has been adduced to show that the climate of Baluchistan in about 2000 B.C. was wetter than that of today, though no measure of the increased wetness has been hazarded. An erroneous interpretation of certain structures—erroneous because hydrologically impossible—started a series of chain-reactions all of which were superficially plausible and all, or so it was claimed, pointed to a wetter climate. The faunal evidence has already been discussed and most of the rest, consisting of dams, terraces, the use of burnt bricks, the density of prehistoric settlement, the use of drains, abundance of fuel for burning bricks, will be discussed in Part III.

One piece of evidence is of a more general interest and illustrates the need for taking account of the whole hydrological picture. Around Quetta in Baluchistan there are many sites of a people, or series of evolving people, generally known as the Quetta culture. The mounds that are now the only visible sign of its settlements are generally on the valley floor and fairly near the Quetta Lora (river). This is now almost dry and marked only by the moist greenness of its bed until, north of Quetta, it flows perennially away to the north. The land around the mounds is mostly either *Khushkab* (dry-farming) or *Sailaba* (watered by diversion of hillside run-off): large patches of orchard and vegetable garden are irrigated by pumps or by *Karezes*. These last are the same as the Persian *Qanat* and consist of long tunnels excavated at a very flat slope at considerable depths in the alluvial valley-fill. They start as an open cutting somewhere fairly low down on the valley-fill side slope and are then driven as tunnels, with access shafts every 20 metres or so for disposal of excavated material, toward the flanking mountain sides; and particularly towards those places where a seasonal torrent emerges from the mountains with a large terminal fan. There are hundreds of *Karezes* in the Quetta valley continually extracting underground water from where the water table is at a higher level along the foot of the mountain and diverting it on to gardens. There, in the process of growing crops, it is evaporated and transpired. All this quite considerable total amount of water originally emerged as springs along the Quetta Lora which consequently had perennial flow.

Many of the Quetta culture sites are fairly high above the Quetta Lora and it has been argued that they could not have survived by an almost dry river unless higher rainfall made dry-farming easier or supplied perennial springs. It has also been argued that the frequency of the mounds shows that conditions were much easier. This second argument is hardly worth refuting for, apart from about 20,000 inhabitants of Quetta itself who all need drinking water, some of which comes from wells, the farming communities of today must be just as numerous as they were in the third millennium B.C. The first argument entirely overlooks the effect of introducing the *Karez*: the date of this is unknown but it was certainly after the end of the Quetta culture. I should think that probably the Quetta culture people practised primitive irrigation along the river, and dry-farming supplemented by *Sailaba* elsewhere. In fact they farmed in almost exactly the same way as the modern people. If the driving of more and more *Karezes*, each one at a lower level in order to obtain a share of a far from unlimited commodity, goes on unchecked the wheel will turn full circle. For all the *Karezes* would ultimately reach a depth at which they could only discharge into the Quetta Lora, restoring its perennial flow.

In Afghanistan, at a certain site, the existence of a chalcolithic well has been cited as evidence of a falling water-table due to desiccation: falling water-table certainly, but due to *Karezes* and not climate. Whenever the evidence seems to point to a failing water supply the temptation seems to be to blame the climate. Sometimes it should not need a specialist to diagnose other causes, but it evidently does.

If prehistorians in general would, without necessarily accepting the correctness of the no climate change hypothesis, at least admit the possibility that there has been no major secular climate change for about 9,000 years, it would stimulate everybody concerned into seeking other causes for whatever they now ascribe to climate.

10 HUMAN ECOLOGY

I have sketched in the scope and limitations of hydrology and its relationships with some other disciplines; I have reviewed some existing ideas that conflict with the principles of the behaviour of water and weather; I have proposed a different weather, or climate, hypothesis; and I have indicated a few of the ways in which the use of simple hydrological principles can help in interpreting the prehistoric environment and in avoiding error. Now it is time to do a kind of flash-back to ecology and put man in the picture as part product of, part reason for, his environment.

There was little, if any, distinction between human ecology and ecology in general until man in one way or another learned to control his environment. The use of tools and weapons to dig up edible roots, kill animals, break open shells and nuts was not ecologically different in kind from the use that other animals made of highly adapted claws or teeth. Even the discovery of fire probably did not for a long time lead to its use as an aid to hunting, but its accidental uncontrolled use increased the incidence of fire as a biotic factor.

Human ecology may have seemed to diverge from the general background when man became an over-efficient predator, but in fact this was merely one aspect of the inexorable law of adjustment. Man killed without thought for the future: food supplies were reduced in one direction and he had to change either his diet or his home, or both.

The true divergence came much later with the introduction of agriculture and herding and the imperative need for man to try to control the vagaries of his environment instead of just running away from them.

In the immediate post-glacial, man had reached a stage of development described variously as late Palaeolithic or Mesolithic on a somewhat arbitrary basis. Wherever man was at that time, he was pursuing a hunting and food-gathering economy. Where game animals were plentiful his economy differed little from that of the middle Palaeolithic except that his weapons and tools were somewhat more refined. Where large game animals were becoming scarce for any reason man seems to have selected a variety of alternative foods according to his situation: smaller animals and birds, fruits, even snails, and probably cereals and pulses where they grew wild. I have not included fish and molluscs as these, in particular localities, do not seem to have belonged to any one stage of development. When man switched his hunting to smaller game he may have been stimulated to develop new 'communal' techniques and new small weapons, for it is to a late phase associated with smaller game that the beginning of most microlithic industries is related. The reasons for scarcity of large game probably varied from place to place. In the northern forests, whatever their vegetation climax, large game probably continued to be plentiful for a long time: they were indeed still fairly plentiful for a very much larger population well into historic times, though by then the larger population was not dependent on the chase.

In the Near and Middle East the change from full glacial conditions to those of 7000 B.C. and today were probably more ecologically decisive than they were farther north. A change of mean rainfall from 500 to 300 mm. per annum, although equal in quantity to that from 1,000 to 800 mm. per annum, implies a decisive change from open Mediterranean woodland to semi-desert steppe, whereas the other does not necessarily imply any major ecological change. Changes from forest to open woodland or from this to semi-desert steppe would have brought with them faunal changes, different hunting conditions, and the need for a fairly fundamental readjustment of the economy. It is probably no accident that, in the Near and Middle East, man seems at that time to have started systematically collecting the ancestors of our modern cereals and pulses; and it is possibly no accident that these cultigens themselves may have first appeared then. Their appearance may have been a response through natural selection to relative desiccation in the immediate post-glacial and could have happened in any of the many interglacial periods. In fact, other similar potential cultigens may have evolved in past interglacial periods and disappeared either through inability to adapt to relatively 'pluvial' conditions, in the sense described earlier, or through inability to re-adapt later to drier conditions by moving against the force of gravity when rainfall isohyets moved uphill at the end of 'pluvial' conditions.

Botanical evolution is a matter for the specialist but it is still fairly safe to say that natural selection is the essential mechanism, despite some doubts inspired by the time-scale of evolutionary change. Little is known with certainty of the rate of production of mutations and even less about the interaction of physical environment and mutations. What seems clear, perhaps misleadingly so, to the non-botanist is that, irrespective of the cause of the rate of production of mutations of all kinds, the chances of certain mutations surviving must surely be improved under conditions of rapid change of environment. For instance, chance mutations affording better adaptation to a more arid or more rainy climate would have little hope of survival unless a change to more arid or more rainy conditions occurred of which they could take advantage. It would be interesting to know to what extent the environmental changes of short duration, arising out of the built-in variability of climatic parameters, afford opportunities for mutation survival. It is precisely in the habitat of the wild cultigens that we have the combination of very high rainfall variability, and of rainfall minima that stop short of wholesale destruction by drought. Mutation on the part of certain grasses towards xerophytic characteristics—heavy fruiting, ability of the seed to remain alive for long periods, minimal leafing, and the right kind of root structure—may have been going on all through the Pleistocene in response to rainfall variability, and may have been additionally stimulated by overall drying of the climate in each post-glacial period.

The archaeological evidence does not indicate the existence of noble grasses before the Holocene though this does not mean they did not exist. On the other hand there seems to be some common-sense reason for supposing that the present noble grasses evolved rapidly during the immediate post-glacial climate change under the double stimulus of overall change and rainfall variability; and that earlier noble grasses failed to survive the succession of 'pluvial' and desiccation.

If so, we have the interesting possibility that man's transition from hunting to the collection of noble grasses and other cultigens, and thence to agriculture, was a historical imperative dictated by the convergent effects of physical environmental change on him and on his sources of food. Animal sources of food dwindled in response to the same changes that produced high-energy vegetable substitutes. It is fascinating to speculate on the influence that this change to major reliance on a high-energy food had on man's subsequent development. It cannot be entirely coincidence that development accelerated when his diet changed; perhaps through another historical imperative, that of the inevitable need of social organisation in order to take advantage of the new foods. If this smacks of environmental determinism it also concerns a period before man's full emergence as a social being, when environment was as determinant of man as of other animals.

The known habitats of the wild Eurasian cultigens today are, with few exceptions, in the hills or mountains that form the northern margin of the so-called *fertile crescent.* Thus, all along the hills of Palestine, of eastern Lebanon, of Syria, Turkey, Iraq, and at least the western aspect of the Zagros in Iran, evidence is found of wild wheat and barley, pulses, etc. Similar evidence is found in certain locations in the Balkans that are outside the fertile crescent, and a different wild barley has been claimed from northern Afghanistan. There are three basic similarities between all these situations. Firstly they lie almost entirely within the strip of country bounded by the 300 mm. and 500 mm. isohyets. (Isohyets are lines on a map joining points of equal rainfall, whether it be the rainfall of a single storm, of a month, a season, a year or the mean of a stated period of years.) Secondly, they all lie within a zone where rainfall follows a marked seasonal pattern; in this case, with winter rain and summer drought. Thirdly, all experience high year-to-year variation of rainfall.

It has already been argued that mean rainfall figures can be misleading by themselves, but throughout the Middle East the means are fairly reliable indicators of many characteristics superimposed upon the all-important background of seasonality. For instance, the incidence of periods of drought during the season of rainfall, however such periods may be quantitatively defined, increases with decreasing rainfall. This is not as obvious as it might sound. For an annual rainfall of, let us say, 350 mm. all concentrated into six months of the year could mean some rain every day with daily totals averaging about 2 mm.—in fact conditions not unlike those of south-east England all the year round, where periods of more than a few days without rain are rare, whether in winter or summer, and the daily average is of this order. It could equally, and in fact does, mean in the Middle East and southern Mediterranean, short periods of relatively heavy rain separated by long periods, often three or four weeks at a time, with no rain. Rain almost every day is more often than not accompanied by a high percentage of cloud cover during the whole of every day, with consequent low insolation, relatively high humidity, and low evaporation losses. When rain occurs fairly heavily over short, widely separated periods, a degree of cloudiness certainly characterises these short periods but is rare during the long separating intervals. During these there is more insolation (more effective also because of the low latitude), less humidity and more evaporation. The combined effects in a normal year are generally not disastrous simply because all factors are muted by winter conditions. So 350 mm. of rainfall in the Middle East is generally more effective for vegetation than the same amount in the Sudan, other things (and particularly soils) being equal. Similarly, the same amount of rainfall over the same period is more effective for vegetation in England than in the Middle East. In short there is a relationship between mean rainfall and drought in the Middle East.

There is also a relationship between year-to-year variability of rainfall and the mean annual rainfall which is particularly discernible in the semi-arid and arid areas of the Middle East. At sites in Jordan and Iraq, for example, each having a mean annual rainfall of 300 mm., the minima and maxima corresponding to a certain frequency of recurrence will be approximately the same and so will the incidence of drought. I have already explained why the climax vegetation is dependent more on minima and the incidence of drought than on other factors, and so one would expect to find, for the same soil conditions in the two countries, the same natural vegetation climax. This is borne out in practice today, and seems to be borne out by the evidence of the ancestors of our cereals and pulses which are everywhere associated with approximately the same mean annual rainfall.

The map reproduced as Pl. 14 shows the 300 mm. and 500 mm. isohyets of today and the distribution of known sites of the earliest Neolithic settlements dependent on dry-farming; that is, on farming without benefit of irrigation. With few exceptions, which I will come to shortly, the sites lie within this isohyetal strip which also defines the approximate boundaries of the wild cereal habitat. If I mention only the cereals, it is for simplicity. In fact, they shared their habitat with a number of other cultigens, such as pulses and seeds yielding oil, and overlapped the modern habitat of pistachio. At Jarmo the discovery of evidence of wild grains in levels dated to the early Neolithic can only be interpreted as indicating the use of the same wild cereals that still survive today around the site wherever grazing has not wiped them out.

It seems logical to assume that the first attempts to sow cereals, whatever may have been the accident or conscious reasoning that led to them, would have taken place in the habitat of the cereals. For, without irrigation, cultivation would have failed in a drier habitat, and in a wetter habitat the cultivation would have been choked by weeds better adapted than the cereals to higher rainfall. So the first transitions from harvesting to sowing would have involved very little change apart from some increase in man's identification with a certain piece of land as his personal or tribal property. The existence of Mesolithic settlements, based on harvesting, implies that already the idea of ownership of the wild fruits had taken hold of men's minds, for surely no one would go to the trouble of constructing a settlement, even if it were only seasonally occupied, without being reasonably sure of his title to the harvest.

The habitual distinction between Mesolithic and Neolithic is really very blurred and there is no reason for supposing that the gradual transition took place simultaneously over wide areas. There is even less reason to suppose that it affected all the people in any one area. It is easily arguable that the first to undertake the transition were the weaker brethren, those less hardy, less skilled in the chase. The majority may have pursued a hunting and collecting economy for centuries or millennia. Their hunting and collecting were restricted only by the need for drinking water. They may even have despised the farmers, much as the modern *bedu* despises the *fellah.* Not everyone, even in Western countries today, is convinced that the ancient and decisive step to farming that led, seemingly inevitably, to ulcers, the rat-race and the threat of nuclear war, was a good one. But of course the despised farmers, like the modern fellah, had to tighten their belts less often, had a better diet and soon a surplus and eventually it was they who despised the Mesolithic semi-nomads. There are modern parallels.

It is important to avoid the kind of over-simplification implicit in the comparison between modern fellah and bedu and the prehistoric situation. For a start, the bedu are not in the least like the hunting-food-gathering Mesolithic people and indeed are only nomadic in a limited sense. The bedu do hunt (so do stockbrokers), but their economy is largely pastoral supplemented by certain specialised forms of gathering that which they did not sow, and by a simple form of distributive activity, particularly along desert routes. They have inevitably been relegated to the deserts, where they have acquired a degree of adaptation to desert life that gives them a large advantage. Their specialised collecting depends on where they live and is seldom for their own direct use. For instance, they are the collectors and carriers of salt in areas such as the southern Libyan desert; they play a part in the collection of gum-arabic and of frankincense; and their ancestors almost certainly took part in the mining of those minerals that were found in the deserts, and the carriage of them to centres where they were to be processed. At the same time, they certainly were, and occasionally still are, parasitic on settled communities to the extent that they sometimes helped themselves to the produce of the latter without giving anything in return; and nowadays they are a source of casual seasonal labour in the settlements. Their combination of partial self-sufficiency and of serving, and occasionally robbing, the settled people was facilitated by their adoption of the camel.

The Mesolithic people in the cultural sense, those who started from a food-gathering and hunting economy and persisted in it for as long as freedom to range was not interfered with by large-scale expansion of cultivation, were probably the last true nomads. They were not restricted merely to areas incapable of cultivation as the bedu are, and they were not tied originally by the needs of flocks and herds. Although their living must have been always precarious, they had mobility as a protection against local droughts and famines.

Very early in the history of settlements, those who abandoned nomadism would almost inevitably have begun to experience the handicaps, such as vulnerability to drought, inherent in increased reliance on the seasonal availability of certain wild foods. Where they built settlements in or near the wild harvest areas they had already taken the first step towards the Neolithic, but even without such settlements a regular seasonal pattern of movement would have begun to form, dependent on the locations and dates of ripening of their wild crops and on availability of water to drink. Whether they or settled collectors were the first, in the Middle East, to practise pastoralism is still not known with certainty, and we do not know whether agriculture preceded herding or the other way round. As both activities must have depended for their inception on chance conjunctions of stimulus and opportunity within the limits of environmental possibility, it may be that in one place herding came first and in another agriculture. When herding was an incipient adjunct to a basically hunting and collecting economy it introduced a new factor into nomadism by adding the need for grazing or browsing areas and more plentiful water supplies. Freedom to wander at will must have been severely reduced and a primitive form of transhumance would have taken place. Some of those practising it may have taken the next step—of cultivating what they had been accustomed to collect.

If herding came later than agriculture in some areas, it could have been a result of as yet only partial reliance on cultivated crops or it could have been an idea borrowed from neighbours who had themselves developed herding first.

Whether agriculture or herding came first can be guessed at on environmental grounds. The situations suitable for the beginnings of agriculture—the natural habitats of the cultigens—were not only restricted to a narrow rainfall belt but also to suitable ecological situations within that belt. These had to have the particular combination of length of growing season (mostly determined by altitude), soil, aspect, and so on in which the cultigens could flourish at the expense of other herbaceous species, and each situation must have been within reach of a reliable supply of drinking water. The choice must have been fairly limited. The situations suited to grazing covered a much larger area, from desert steppe (associated with as little as 100 mm. mean annual rainfall and affording seasonal grazing) to fairly dense woodland with clearings (associated with perhaps as much as 800 mm. mean annual rainfall). The area available was vastly greater than that for rain farming.

I do not for a moment suggest that man the herdsman consciously worked out that he could live on the flesh and milk of animals, which could use large areas of vegetation unsuitable for direct consumption by him; but the relative assurance of food, even if it were not as efficient a food as the cereals and pulses, must have affected man's choice unconsciously. This, the much greater range of physical and botanical environment available, and the mobility of herded sources of food, must surely weight the odds in favour of pastoralism having preceded agriculture.

Can we learn anything from the so-called nomadism of today? Not very much, I think. It is neither true nomadism nor the lineal descendent of Mesolithic nomadism. Most of it is either semi-nomadism or transhumance, and these are similar only in that both are seasonal, and that both require a fixed base or bases. Some modern peoples practise both and certainly both activities are often pursued by different people in the same area. The often parasitic desert people who survive on a combination of raiding and trading also require a fixed base, but they are a very special case. To the extent that they depend upon raiding, or did until recently, they have reverted to a special form of hunting and collecting—of the fruits of other people's labour in the form of horses, camels, grain and the rest—made possible because their ancestors had at some stage domesticated the camel. Their way of life would be impossible without the inherited knowledge of camel-raising and without the existence of more advanced 'host' communities to provide a large part of their needs.

Those who practise semi-nomadism belong in almost all cases to tribes or communities with a mixed economy that have a settled centre or centres at which agriculture is practised. The herdsmen of the community wander with their sheep, goats, camels, and sometimes cattle, within a range that is defined by ancient community rights and by the availability of drinking water for them and their animals from rivers, springs, wells, or seasonal ponds. Their range is generally within one climatic habitat, and this is possible because fodder is available during the dry season from crop residues, local grazing niches along streams, or by going a few hundred metres up into mountains within their range; sometimes the dried but still standing grasses provide sufficient nourishment and can be used if they are within walking distance of water. Good examples of this form of semi-nomadism can be found in the medium-altitude area of Baluchistan known as Jhalawan and in the Sudan. The same people, however, practise transhumance when their range cannot support their animals and also, particularly nowadays, when there is the added attraction of paid seasonal work elsewhere.

Transhumance involves wholesale removal of herds from one habitat to another and back on a seasonal basis. It is almost always linked to a settlement at one end of the transhumance axis and to a defined and fairly permanent area of interest, sometimes settled by other members of the same tribe or community, at the other end. It is generally dictated as much by non-hydrologic climate factors such as temperature, as by availability of fodder which is indirectly a hydrologic factor.

In the western Sudan the Baggara cattle-rearing Arabs migrate north from their good grasslands in southern Darfur and Kordofan at the outset of the rains and follow the rains, and the grass they produce, for two or three hundred kilometres. They leave their homeland, because of the sticky heat and the swarms of flies, for an area that is only slightly cooler but much drier and less fly-ridden. At the north end of their axis they have to compete with the semi-nomadic element of settled sudanic tribes, but the competition is controlled by custom and limited by the fact that the settled tribes naturally choose permanent wells while the Baggara camp around seasonal lakes and ponds.

Farther north, in the same two provinces of the Sudan, the camel-raising Arabs move northwards out of their normal area (the northern end of the Baggara axis) into the *gizzu*. Both are practising transhumance. In Jordan the bedu move southward in the winter, and return north in the summer.

In Baluchistan and Afghanistan the extreme cold of the winter, rather than the shortage of grazing, causes a wholesale removal of herds from the high plateau areas down to the Indus Valley or to any intermediate place where the competition is not too keen. The Baluchis often have a secondary tribal area, with a fixed population, on the plains of the Indus Valley or Las Bela. There their animals survive on browse provided by the thin jungle cover of uncultivated areas, and on crop residues. The Powindars of Afghanistan, mainly members of Pashtu-speaking tribes that are divided by a political frontier, compete with the Baluchis and normally have no relations to go to. Incidentally, transhumance is practised by much of the human population of Quetta in order to avoid the cold. The convoys of thousands of horse-drawn *gharris* going to Sibi each autumn and returning each spring are an unforgettable sight. Until recently the government of Kalat state did the same thing, moving all its staff and their files from Kalat to Dhadar and back each year.

These illustrations are given simply because they show the diversity of background of semi-nomadism and transhumance and their basic difference from Mesolithic-type nomadism. Modern movements of this kind are indeed often dictated by climate, and particularly by rainfall and water supplies, but these are the only factors shared with Mesolithic man.

The fundamental physical requirements of man are now, as always, food and water. Of these water in an arid climate is geographically limited, while food, given a readiness to be virtually omnivorous, can be found in one form or another within reach of almost any permanent water supply. The paramount factor, indeed the determining factor, in man's choice of either a nomadic circuit or a settled home, must therefore be water. If the water supply was in or near the habitat of the cultigens, determined in its turn largely by the availability of sufficient water in the form of rainfall, the chances of man advancing sooner or later from harvesting to sowing were good. If the water supply was far from these habitats the chances were that man would sooner or later evolve into a herdsman.

If we assume that at any place rainfall during the farming and/or herding revolution was, within the limits of present variability, the same as that of today, we can go a long way towards deducing from today's data where the revolution or transition took place, by starting from water supply. We already know some places where it took place but there are enormous geographical gaps. I say advisedly that we can go a long way, and I do not claim that we can now identify all the places where perennial water was formerly available. For, although the rainfall means are almost certainly the same now as they were then, the rest of the hydrologic régime may have changed considerably. Some areas that could, on the basis of today's rainfall, be forested, have been denuded by over-browsing or fire or cutting and the run-off characteristics will almost certainly have changed. This could have affected the amount of infiltration and this would affect, in its turn, the flow of perennial streams and springs. Such changes would be particularly likely in areas characterised by high intensity rainfall. Areas like Jordan, with comparatively low intensity rainfall, would be little affected.

There does not seem to be any evidence so far of any early Neolithic site that was dependent wholly on herding, and what evidence there is points to herding as an adjunct to either hunting or agriculture. This does not contradict the possibility that herding may have preceded agriculture, but does suggest that *settlements* based wholly or mainly on herding are unlikely. For herding requires a large range of country with grazing and suitably dispersed water points and is not much helped by a fixed centre. I do not infer from this that herding settlements did not exist or that they will not be found, but merely that they are considerably less likely. The moment that a herding economy was wedded to agriculture, a fixed settlement became essential and its location would be determined by agricultural requirements, water supply and availability of grazing.

It is reasonable to deduce, both from the evidence illustrated in Pl. 13 and from theoretical considerations, that settlements based on the first attempts to collect crops will be found between the modern isohyets that represent the rainfall range of the cultigens or in habitat niches in higher or lower rainfall, where soil and other conditions redress the balance. These niches will include the neighbourhood of springs or shallow ground-water areas in low rainfall zones where the effect of higher rainfall is simulated. Within these areas, settlement must have been restricted to places that now have a perennial source of surface water, or that could then have had one with different run-off conditions.

The identification of what could have been is not as difficult as it may seem. Where there is perennial surface water now, it is perfectly safe to assume that there was so then, and perhaps in greater quantity. Where there is no surface water today and no wells as evidence of shallow ground-water, it is fairly safe to assume that there was no perennial water then. If a stream that drains an area capable of sustaining forest or woodland, but now denuded, carries water for several months during the rains, it is likely that it was no worse then. A competent hydrologist should be able to estimate the prehistoric situation if he has access to rainfall data including intensity data. Almost any spring or line of seepage that is today perennial could have afforded a supply. It does not require much more than a wet patch on a hillside, now choked with vegetation and debris, to provide the human drinking needs of a small community.

In deducing where settlements could have been it is essential to know what use is being made of water today. Often it will be found that water is now being diverted for irrigation purposes, that mechanical pumps have been installed in shallow wells, or that water is being extracted in other ways, so that what is apparently available today does not represent the whole of what was once available. Some streams that are now dry would flow today if extraction and diversions were stopped. Examples of this sort of thing from Petra and other sites will be described later.

There are, therefore, two essential things to investigate, both of which, for their proper assessment, require a knowledge of hydrology: the rainfall characteristics and the existence of perennial water. Any place in the southern Mediterranean–Middle East climate zone that is within the right rainfall bracket, and has or had perennial water, is a potential settlement site for the period of transition from harvesting to sowing and is worth investigating.

It is interesting to speculate on the various steps that could have led from simple clearing of the ground, probably by burning off the weeds, to preparing it in even the most elementary way: but it is mostly irrelevant to this book. One relevant factor, because it depends on climate, is the long time-gap between harvesting and sowing. Harvesting generally takes place in the Middle East between April and early June according to the altitude and latitude. From then until October or November, when the first rain can be expected, the ground is too hard to dig, too dry to germinate the seed. The first rains can be disastrous if they are heavy enough to germinate the seed but not sufficient to provide the moisture needs of the seedlings. If, as often happens, there is a dry period of several weeks following the first rain much, if not all, of the crop can be lost. The peculiar characteristics of Middle East rainfall must have made the transition from harvesting to sowing a difficult and sometimes heart-breaking affair.

Once cultivation had started, the variability of rainfall from one year to another must have gradually led the early cultivators to two conclusions. The first was that the neighbourhood of springs, the margins of small streams, and the areas flooded annually by rivers with flood plains, were all obviously and in that order less vulnerable to lack of rain. The second was that up the hill in the higher rainfall areas to which hunting may have taken them, the effects of drought years were far less marked. At a very early stage wandering bands of Mesolithic men must have encountered flood-plain situations when they followed game downhill during the winter. In these situations there must have been sporadic occurrences of wild cereals whose seeds had been washed down by floods. The cereals were probably seldom dense enough in such locations to justify collection. Even if they were sometimes collected they would hardly have encouraged permanent settlement. Later, when cultivation had become accepted, the lessons of clearing and preparing the land learned in the cereals' natural habitat could have been applied to land seasonally flooded, and it is probably in some such way that the idea of irrigation was born. In the higher rainfall areas, fields less vulnerable to drought could have been cultivated once the techniques of weed control had been learnt, but both this and irrigation cultivation had to await the development of fairly efficient tools. In the case of some inundation situations, it would have been necessary too to learn how to dig for drinking water in the dry season; and in all such places some knowledge of how to control flood damage would have been necessary before there could be real development. In the case of the higher rainfall areas, the move uphill could sometimes have meant, rather paradoxically, going above the perennial streams or springs on which their drinking water supply depended.

Both moves, therefore, required a knowledge of better cultivation techniques and of some ability to control or diversify their water supply. The distribution map reproduced as Pl. 10 shows how these movements appear to be related to the fairly highly developed chalcolithic period, and indicates that man's choice of settlement sites had then already become much wider and much more subject to his control. By the early Bronze Age man's control of water and his agricultural knowledge had already taken him to most areas in the Middle East where agriculture is practised today.

The broad conclusion to be drawn from these premises is very pertinent to the question of diffusion versus parallel development. In man's hunting and collecting phase in the late Palaeolithic and Mesolithic, his freedom to wander where he wished was very little restricted and was probably helped also by the existence of land bridges due to marine regression. Those communities which, in the late Mesolithic, and early Neolithic, sold their birthright of wandering for a mess of barley potage, became prisoners within their settlement areas as soon as they came to rely on cereals and other cultigens as their staple diet, whether these were systematically collected or cultivated. The scarcity of suitable places, their isolation geographically along deeply dissected escarpments, by major rivers or desert tracts, must all surely have conspired towards development in isolation, with the results that one sees of apparent lack of ceramic and other cultural contacts. The dates of the beginnings of such isolated development may have varied from place to place according to local availability of different foods, but the fact of isolation seems inescapable and would surely have favoured parallel development.

As soon as Neolithic man had begun to control his environment and widen his choice of site, isolation would no longer have been necessary, and by the late Neolithic, e.g. Halafian, times cultural and even trade contacts made possible the diffusion of ideas and skills. The situation must undoubtedly have been complex in practice and particularly so when people, already at a mobile late Neolithic stage, expanded into the areas of those less developed.

It has sometimes been suggested that the underdeveloped matrix of Mesolithic cultures, in which the farming revolution took place, could have provided cultural links. It is, of course, possible, but a comparison with modern semi-nomadic pastoralists is valid here. These people do not have much use for earthenware pots that are easily broken, and with difficulty replaced, during their wanderings: they prefer baskets, metal, or skins. They are by definition and choice unskilled in settled agriculture. Pottery and knowledge of agriculture and how to build, culturally define a prehistoric settled community, and it seems improbable that Neolithic nomads, having no need of two of these skills and no knowledge of the third, would have been vectors of ideas. They may have traded such things as obsidian and flint, the use of which they shared already with the settled people, but that must have been about the limit of cultural contact. For their containers they probably used animal skins for water and basketry for other purposes.

The correlation between mean annual rainfall and prehistoric settlement is, at first sight, contradicted by two (and possibly more) notable exceptions: one of them will be described in more detail in a later chapter. The exceptions are

Jericho and El Beidha, both in Jordan. Both of them enjoy, if any place can be said to enjoy such conditions of drought, mean rainfalls of less than 200 mm. and therefore, unless the climate has undergone a radical change since their first Neolithic occupations in the seventh millennium B.C., neither could have been in the natural habitat of the wild cereals. At Jericho, however, there is the very large spring called 'Ain es Sultan, and an area which, on the basis of rainfall, could be a habitat for the wild cereals is not more than ten kilometres distant. We do not, in fact, know with certainty whether the people of Jericho in the Neolithic period were already practising agriculture, but in the preceding Mesolithic period they probably were not. As the rainfall of Jericho in Mesolithic times, because of its situation in a classical rain shadow, is unlikely to have been so much more than that of today as to provide a wild cereal habitat, the site was probably occupied primarily because of its abundant supply of water; and the inhabitants may have gone up into the hills towards Jerusalem for the collection of grain. If in the succeeding Neolithic the inhabitants started cultivation, it is possible that they also, simultaneously and unconsciously, started irrigation farming. The waters of 'Ain es Sultan, issuing without control by man, would have created a fairly extensive area where cultivation would have been possible on soil in which the moisture was not dependent on rainfall.

At Beidha, some 240 kilometres to the south, it seems possible that the Neolithic people were already cultivating in 6800 B.C., so it is possible that cultivation was already practised at Jericho at the same time. Jericho, therefore, is probably one of those places already referred to where a combination of soil and ground-water created a habitat niche in which the ecological effect of higher rainfall was simulated. At Beidha, where there is a marked gap between the Mesolithic and the Neolithic, migration from the natural habitat zone may have been already completed in the earliest Neolithic. There is some evidence that 9,000 years ago the now almost completely denuded valley at El Beidha had still a considerable valley fill of fine alluvium. The proximity of large areas of rock and the fact that the valleys, filled with alluvium, occupied only a small proportion of the total area, would have conspired to concentrate run-off on the alluvium, giving the effect of considerably higher rainfall. The only problem at Beidha would have been drinking water, but it was no more of a problem for the Neolithic people than it was in the winter of 1964 for Miss Kirkbride's expedition, when water was fetched daily from a distance of about five kilometres from a series of springs up on the escarpment. It may be relevant that the escarpment, from the level of the springs upwards and eastwards and extending to the shallow valley on the east side, has even today sufficient rainfall to form a potential habitat for the wild cereals. It is possible, therefore, that a transition from food gathering to cultivation could have already taken place almost anywhere on the escarpment ridge behind Beidha. This extends from south of Wadi Musa to north of the Sea of Galilee and Mount Hermon. In this case the settlement was established at El Beidha partly because of the availability of reasonable soil and run-off from the adjoining rocks, and partly because of the apparent abundance of game. The enormous quantities of bones and horns found in the excavations appear to be evidence of this.

However the change to farming and herding came about, the change itself started an escape from environmental determinism. The first farmers, cultivating with the help of rainfall only, were dependent wholly on their environment: indeed by sharing the immobility of crops they became the prisoners of their environment. In finding ways of controlling water or of destroying competing vegetation (weeds) man initially responded to the stimulus of hunger, but from that moment human ecology became a separate and different thing in which one element—man—gradually exerted conscious control—both good and bad—over the face of the earth for the first time in the earth's history.

Some of the methods that prehistoric man used have already been described and some are described in the following chapters. The examples illustrated range from the earliest pre-pottery Neolithic to the largest of all chalcolithic civilisations, that of the Indus Valley.

Outstanding examples of man-induced environmental change are: deforestation for cultivation, large-scale herding of grazing animals, terracing to preserve soil and run-off, diversion of flood water or perennial flow for irrigation, the use of the *Karez*, and the sinking of wells for drinking water and other purposes.

The early steps in man's control of his environment were all, as far as the old world is concerned, taken in the Middle East. By the time that farming was introduced into northern Europe it was already highly developed (from Middle-Eastern origins), and the only adaptation required was that of raising, in cold and wet climates, cereals whose ancestors were developed in the warm, dry fertile crescent. This is an almost exclusively botanical problem but it is relevant to note here that cereals in northern climates, where a period of winter dormancy coincides with much of the rainfall, probably do not make use of much more rain than that on which their ancestors lived.

PART III

CASE STUDIES

11 CASES INVOLVING HYDROLOGY AND CLIMATE

When the investigations described in this and the next chapter were first undertaken I started with nothing more than a vague feeling that there was something technically wrong with the generally accepted interpretations of prehistoric climates.

I was in Baluchistan at the time and my normal work took me over much of the ground covered by Sir Aurel Stein and described by him in *An Archaeological Tour of Gedrosia* as well as to some places that he did not visit. Some of my journeys had to be undertaken on camels, great, hulking, earth-shaking beasts used normally for carrying merchandise, because of the absence, real or alleged, of jeepable tracks. The camels and their excruciatingly uncomfortable tandem saddles were a sad come-down after the riding animals that I had become used to in the Sudan, which carry a single and improbably comfortable saddle perched on the top of the hump. However, they served their purpose, and had the advantage of lifting one above the sand-fly zone near the ground: and as usual they provided a reasonably elevated view-point. Except on one occasion, when travelling from Khuzdar in the mountains to Shoran on the plains, along what I discovered too late to be a jeepable track, the routes that I followed had little of archaeological interest. That ride down the Mula river valley could have led me to more than twenty prehistoric sites of varying interest but it was a failure in this respect. It was not the fault of the camels but of the extreme heat: I was new to Baluchistan and although quite used to hot weather camelling in other countries, I had failed to make allowances for the mid-summer humidity. The ride was only completed because the means of transport to get me home was at the far end, at Shoran where I had sent the jeep: I achieved nothing during the ride because of heat exhaustion.

This digression about camels is relevant for the negative reason that journeys made with their help yielded little of archaeological interest except in the case of the Mula route. I went by camel only when there did not seem to be a jeepable track. All the major sites that I saw in Baluchistan, which included quite a number that had not hitherto been reported, were on or fairly close to the main modern tracks. These were until fairly recently only camel tracks themselves, and were basically no easier nor more difficult to make suitable for wheeled traffic than those that I used. They differ from these last in one essential particular: without exception they link the main areas where today soil and water can support agriculture. Such areas are, also without exception, those where the remains of prehistoric settlements are found. In the rugged, denuded topography of Baluchistan such areas occupy a comparatively small percentage of the total. Almost all of them are still centres of occupation today, but where they are not so there appears to be no obvious reason, such as lack of water and soil, to explain it. In one very dry area, the Kulli tract, the inhabitants eke out a precarious existence amid many prehistoric mounds, but if the population density today is less than that of 4,000 years ago it may be because the perennial Mashkai river originally flowed through here but was later captured by the Hingol-Nal river system. There is room for considerable doubt about the prehistoric population density, as the numerous mounds listed by Stein cover an impressively long period of prehistory and quite a number of cultures.

Some of this I noticed at the time, some is the result of hindsight. Most new arrivals in Baluchistan and all those with an interest in archaeology were quickly introduced to Stuart Piggott's *Prehistoric India.* I was no exception. I read it first before seeing anything of the archaeology and before obtaining any first-hand knowledge of hydrological conditions. By the time I read it again after about a year it was with some hydrological insight, and the vague feeling that something was wrong was beginning to crystallise. I wrote to Professor Piggott, a letter of some fourteen pages of not very legible manuscript, disputing some of his ideas. As always after any impulsive action, reaction set in. If I could have persuaded the post office at Quetta to let me have my letter back I believe I would have destroyed it. I could see all my hopes of making some contribution to archaeology disappearing before they had even had a start and was genuinely upset at the impertinence of what I had done.

I need not have worried. After a few weeks I had a most courteous reply from Professor Piggott of which the gist impressed me indelibly. Apart from encouraging me to publish my ideas, he told me that his references to climate had been based, as they had to be, on the work of Sir Aurel Stein whom he had had every reason to accept as an authority, but that he was inclined now to agree that I might be right. What impressed me was not so much that archaeologists—several of them, and all of outstanding reputations—should have had to depend on the expert opinions of another, for that was easily understandable; but that such dependence, by its very nature, makes it difficult for an archaeologist to judge the merits of the expert's opinion. For Stein, apart from being an archaeologist himself, was a geographer by profession and could very easily have been qualified to give the right answers: many brilliant hydrologists of today started their careers as geographers. In his day scientific hydrology hardly existed, and to blame him for his rather emphatic conclusions would be rather like blaming Edison for not knowing about radar.

His conclusions, repeated frequently in his fascinating reports to the Government of India, were that there had been a pronounced desiccation of the climate of Baluchistan since chalcolithic times. We now know that the period which he described in this way was the third millennium B.C. He was also of the opinion that desiccation was still on the increase during those between-the-wars years when he was exploring, as part of a steady climatic trend that he claimed to have observed elsewhere and particularly in central Asia.

He based his conclusions on evidence of various kinds: the *gabarbands*, the number of prehistoric settlements in places where only a few villages exist nowadays, the denudation of the country, the low rainfall of today, and finally the depth of deposits in prehistoric mounds as an indication of cultural stability. My first foray into archaeology resulted from a critical analysis of all this evidence and of other evidence from the Indus Valley interpreted by archaeologists in the same sense. The resulting rather petulant original article fortunately caught the attention of Dr Dyson of the University of Pennsylvania. He managed with great skill to tone down the petulance without obscuring the crusading zeal of the original, and added some very authoritative and pertinent evidence from other fields. The result appeared as a joint paper in the *American Anthropologist* with the title 'The Prehistoric Climate of Baluchistan and the Indus Valley'.

The *gabarbands* are not unique to Baluchistan although I think the name is only used there and in the neighbouring parts of Iranian Baluchistan. They are ruined stone structures that are found in two types of situation. In the first they generally run transversely across a normally dry shallow valley: in the second they follow the contours of the lower side slopes of a valley, generally where a dry tributary valley emerges from the hills, and sometimes run parallel and close to the main stream channel. It must have been the first type of situation, and the very few examples of it where the remains are more than 2 metres or so in height, that led Stein to believe that the *gabarbands* were dams. What remains of them suggests that they were built with level tops. Some of those that have survived are hundreds of metres long where the valley is wide enough, and some of the longer ones show varying top levels in steps. In some areas where suitable massive stone is available, boulders up to about two tons in weight are incorporated.

These large boulders are not dressed masonry but rather blocks already squared roughly by geological bedding and jointing. It was argued that their enormous size must have required plentiful labour to move them. This point is worth examining in isolation. A block of two tons weight could be about $60 \times 100 \times 150$ centimetres in size, or any other combination of dimensions giving a volume of about a cubic metre. Assuming that a man can lift and carry over rough ground about one-thirtieth of a ton, sixty men would be required to carry such a block. So obviously it was not simply carried, for at the most ten men could get their hands to it. It is conceivable that the blocks were carried slung from poles, but the kind of trees that could have grown even on a considerably higher rainfall are not such as to provide long, slim, strong poles. However, ten or so men with or without levers could have rolled a block of this kind, or it could have been dragged by men or animals or both. The large blocks are evidence of skill rather than of abundant man-power. The long structures are only evidence of abundant man-power if they were built in one continuous operation, of which there is no evidence. Most of them could have been built in from three weeks to six months by no more than the present available labour.

What has this got to do with climate? Quite a lot according to Stein. He considered that the climate must have been wetter for the land to sustain a sufficiently large population. Perhaps when he was there the local population was at the other end of its transhumance axis: otherwise he could not have made such a statement. The intermontane valleys of Nal, Mashkai, Wadh, Ornach, in the heart of the *gabarband* country, have populations running into a few thousands that have nothing to do, and nowadays do nothing, between the early summer harvest and the late summer sowing: and very little to do at other times of the year.

Stein's argument centred, however, on the identification of a number of these structures as dams. A few of exceptional height, of which the ruins are in a major drainage channel, undoubtedly were. The local people call these structures, 10 to 15 metres high, by the same name. All of these appear, from study of the geomorphology of the channels, to be certainly no older than early Islamic times, and while there is good reason for supposing that they were intended as dams there is no evidence whatever that they survived the first flood. As none of them has any evidence of a spillway and all are built of dry rubble masonry their chances of survival must have been slender indeed. These few doubtful cases apart, the rest of the *gabarbands* do not fulfil any single one of the requirements of a dam. These requirements are that there should be water available to fill it often enough to justify the effort of building; that the capacity should be large enough to avoid a long and costly spillway to cope with the surplus water from occasional large floods; that the structure itself should be reasonably water-tight; that the bed of the reservoir should be impermeable; and last but certainly not least that there should be some reason, such as irrigation, for constructing the dam. The storage capacities of most *gabarbands* are infinitesimal: there is no evidence of any form of spillway at any of them (the sluice-like structures noted by Stein were mostly only a metre or so wide and, whatever else they were, they were not spillways): the structures of dry stone walling and the reservoirs are often sited on gravelly alluvium. I made calculations on the basis of present-day rainfall amounts and intensities, and of estimated frequency of floods, and the results are such that cautious wording would be misleading. I will not say, therefore, that there can be no doubt that these were not dams; I say emphatically that they were not!

As similar structures are still being built today, but more economically of earth, it is amazing that they were not immediately recognised as terraces. The only cultivable soil exists upstream of them, trapped by them, and this is why nowadays the people are able to use earth as a substitute for stone. I saw one particularly illuminating case. At the lower end of a small valley were the ruins of a massive, carefully built, stone *gabarband* and the remains of the soil terrace that it created. A little way upstream was another, slightly less well-built and equally in ruins. Further upstream again were, in succession, a badly ruined, very rough *gabarband* recently repaired with earth and with corn growing on its terrace, and then three more terraces contained by earth banks. Last of all, above the corn on the uppermost terrace, there was the farmer's hut.

Terraces of this particular kind, depending on occasional spates in otherwise dry torrent beds or on local run-off from bare hillsides, are essentially and everywhere an arid-zone phenomenon. Even if they were not, they are not evidence of change of rainfall when the same cultivation methods are associated with both ancient *gabarbands* and modern earth terraces.

Denudation, in areas of low rainfall, is not a sign of increasing desiccation. It seems to be an inescapable consequence of a certain amount and seasonal distribution of rainfall. Removal of soil and surface vegetation is accomplished by a combination of over-grazing and periodic droughts: removal of trees has been mostly accomplished by man. The casual visitor sees only those hill-slopes near roads and tracks and therefore near habitations. These are totally bare of trees. But go a few kilometres up an unfrequented side valley and the trees are still there, probably because it is not worth the effort of cutting them far from a lorry route.

The argument used about the alleged greater density of prehistoric sites is hardly worth refuting. These little mounds, survivors of a span of perhaps 3,000 years that ended late in the first millennium B.C., had, when they were occupied, populations of probably between 300 and 600 persons, rather smaller on the whole than the modern villages. The latter are probably just as numerous as the villages that were simultaneously occupied at any one period of prehistory. In many tracts the modern villages are both larger in individual area than the ancient ones, and more numerous than all the ancient ones put together. To take an extreme case, the Quetta valley now supports a population that must be many hundreds of times greater than the prehistoric one.

The depth of deposits in the mounds means little unless it has been stratigraphically dug and dated. Where approximate dating has been carried out the evidence appears to be of several hundred years of total, but not necessarily continuous, occupation. Many factors such as earthquakes, an occasional disastrous thunderstorm, exhaustion of soil fertility, and so on could cause intermittent abandonment and the adding of another layer to the thickness of the mound. The similar mounds of lower Mesopotamia did not build up in a wet climate. In fact all the evidence for a wetter climate turned out, on fuller examination, to be more consistent with the persistence for thousands of years of arid conditions similar to those of today.

Stein's views on the chalcolithic climate of Baluchistan inevitably influenced the thinking of those, from Sir John Marshall onwards, who were concerned with the Indus Civilisation. Some saw evidence of major change of the climate, others of only marginal change. Wheeler summed up the feelings of most archaeologists when he wrote in 1953 in *The Indus Civilisation* that '. . . a certain degree of climatic change is beyond dispute. . . .'; though he adds: 'but how far that change is due to "natural causes" and how far to sheer human improvidence (if that be other than a "natural cause") is less easy to say'. His 1953 edition has since been supplanted by that of 1960 in which the statement is qualified by some further doubts about climate change. He tells me that a third edition which is shortly appearing includes my dissenting views.

If there has been a change in opinion since then it has only been towards cautious acceptance of the fact that the degree of climatic change may have been small. As I became more interested and, later, professionally involved in the problem of Mohenjo-daro, it became more and more clear that its climate was not the only aspect requiring a new look. For the moment I will consider the climate evidence and leave the rest to the next chapter.

I assumed that what the scholars meant by climate change in this context was what everyone inferred from their writings, and that was that the change had involved secular, as opposed to temporary, variations. All the sites of the Indus Civilisation in the Indus Valley itself are found on its vast flood-plain, where the mean rainfall of today varies from about 75 mm. per annum in central and northern Sind to about 125 mm. per annum at Harappā on the river Ravi.

The low rainfall is due to two main causes. In winter cold fronts associated with Mediterranean-type depressions occasionally bring cold, moist air to Baluchistan, which accounts for all the winter rain. This is rather more than half the total annual rainfall in the north and rather less than half in the south. The winter mean rainfall is nowhere high and its increase from south to north is partly due to decreasing distance from the associated depression and partly to increasing orographic effect from south to north. The whole of Baluchistan is mountainous with the exception of the Kheran desert, which is a comparatively low plateau, and the Kacchi Plain between Jacobabad and Sibi, which is a re-entrant of the Indus plain. The mountains vary in height from about 1,000 metres in the south to as much as 3,000 metres in the north. Along their lee side, which is occupied by the Indus Valley, there is a pronounced and inescapable Föhn or rain-shadow effect. Westerly air masses are cooled and become more humid, sometimes to the point of yielding some rain, as they are lifted by the mountains. Immediately these air masses

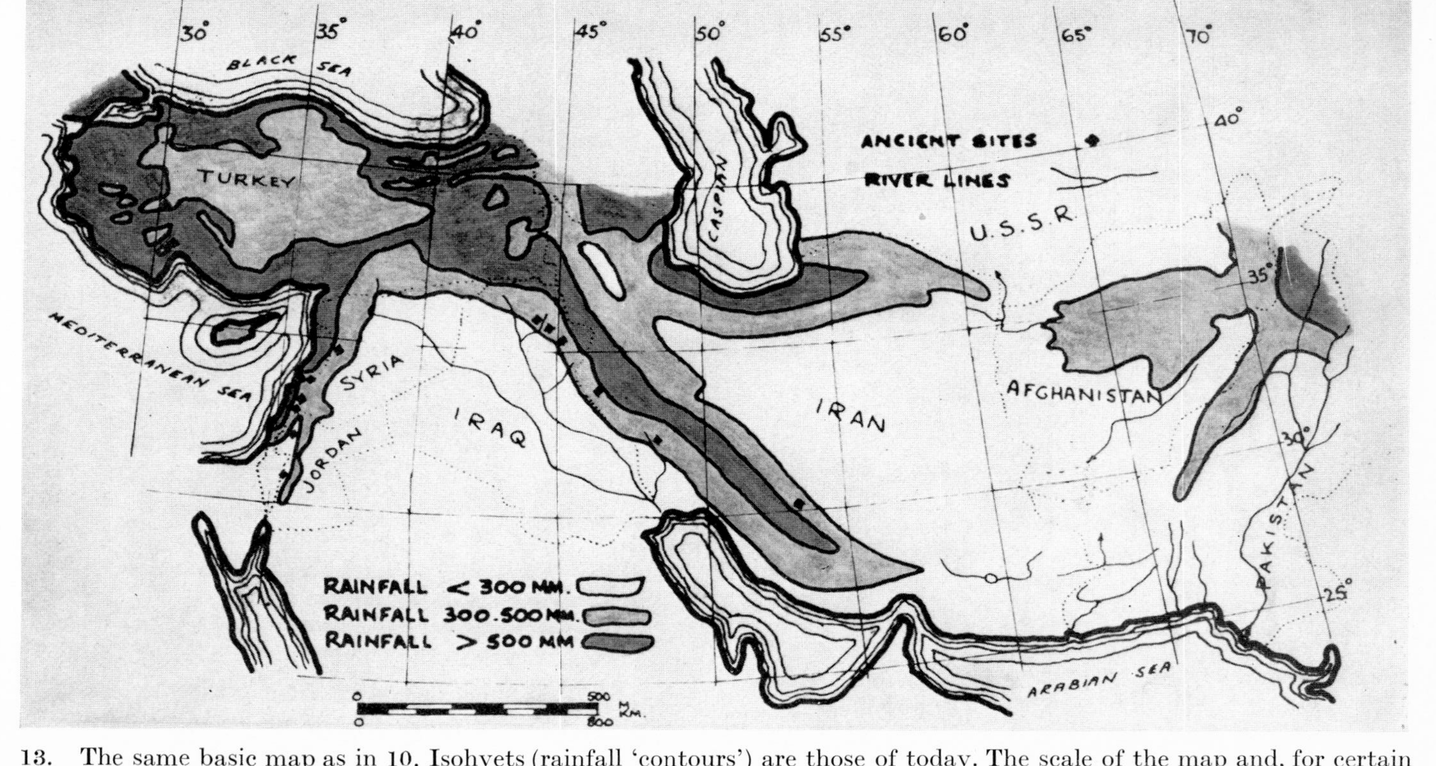

13. The same basic map as in 10. Isohyets (rainfall 'contours') are those of today. The scale of the map and, for certain parts of the area, lack of sufficient reliable data, have made it impossible to indicate more than the general rainfall distribution. For instance, all zones almost certainly contain small isolated areas, particularly near the zonal boundaries, that belong properly to the adjacent zone. Some known Mesolithic *sites* are indicated which mostly fall in or close to the 300–500 mm. zone. While there may be sites falling well outside this zone none has been consciously omitted on that score.

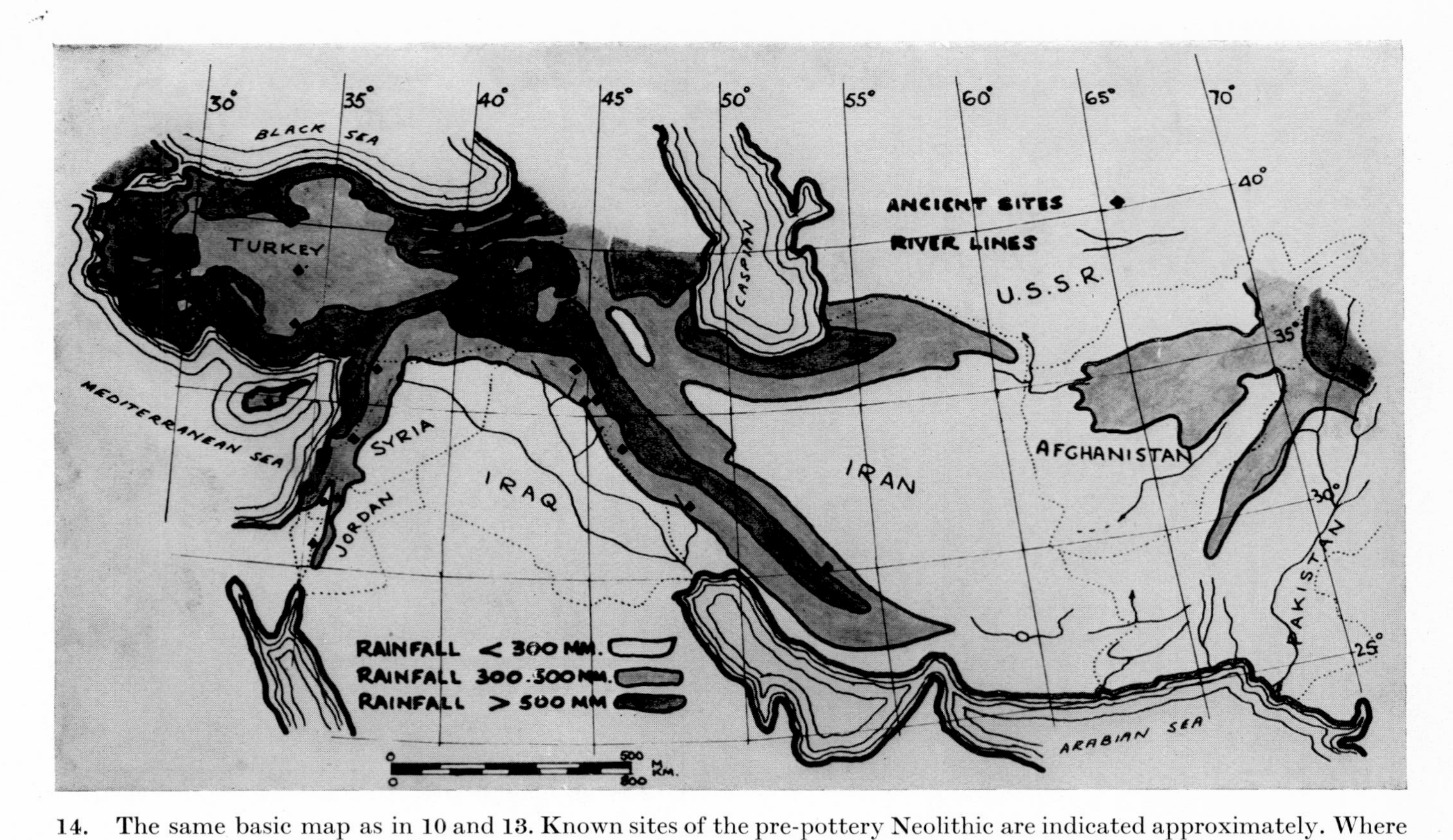

14. The same basic map as in 10 and 13. Known sites of the pre-pottery Neolithic are indicated approximately. Where many sites are grouped in a small area no attempt has been made to indicate all of them. No sites of this period are known to the author that occur in the more-than-500 mm. rainfall zone. One or two occur in the less-than-300 mm. zone

reach the sharp escarpments facing the Indus Valley the air descends and becomes warmer and drier. If the air mass starts by being moist enough it loses some of its none too abundant moisture on the mountains as rain, and when this happens the air descending into the Indus Valley has already become somewhat drier. The situation is such that even were the winter rainfall of Baluchistan considerably higher it is extremely doubtful whether the Indus Valley would obtain any significant benefit, and it is probable that the little rain that occurs at Mohenjo-daro is not due at all to the general air mass movement from the west: it is more probable that it is due to very occasional outbreaks of polar air coming from the north. This is a phenomenon observed elsewhere in the lee of extensive north-south mountain barriers. The causes are somewhat obscure and unpredictable but are thought to be associated with disturbances along the southern boundary of the polar air mass that may have entirely local causes, such as differential heating of the earth's surface. In the winter this polar air mass boundary moves well down over the Indian peninsula. But even such polar outbreaks cannot escape Föhn effect in the Indus Valley. A general southward movement of the polar air mass could result in an increased frequency of polar outbreaks, but there is at present no evidence that it was farther south in chalcolithic times.

The cause of summer rain is quite different. When the land mass from the Indus Valley, westward through Iran, Iraq, and Syria, heats up in the early summer a long, irregular, but persistent area of low pressure builds up. Normal cyclonic circulation occurs around this long strip and some of the moist south-westerly air of equatorial origin, known as the monsoon, is drawn into this circulation. This south-west monsoon current meets the coast in the area between Karachi and Bombay and then swings counter-clockwise around the Indian desert. When it reaches the Punjab it tends to follow the northern edge of the low-pressure zone. It very rapidly becomes modified through heating and through the loss of rain in Rajasthan and the Punjab and soon becomes entirely ineffective as a source of rain. The low summer rainfall of Quetta is due to local circulation in the low-pressure belt, but the effect is negligible further west. No air current behaves entirely predictably and so not all of the monsoon current skirts the desert areas. Some if it is drawn into local circulation and can give rise to the type of local intense convective rain that would result in Mohenjo-daro receiving its whole mean annual rainfall or more in one storm. The configuration of sea areas, mountains, and hot low plains that controls this circulation is unlikely to have changed. The probable climatological background, therefore, does not appear to be in conflict with the archaeological evidence.

It has been said that the use of burnt bricks at Indus Civilisation sites indicated the need for a method of construction more resistant to rain than mud-bricks. The fact that burnt bricks require fuel for the kilns is said to indicate enough rain to support forest. The use of a fairly elaborate drainage system is said to indicate the need to get rid of storm water. I have already mentioned the fauna illustrated on Indus seals and there is no need to go into that again.

The case rests largely on burnt bricks and drains. Burnt bricks, particularly when laid for the most part in mud mortar, are not an indication of the need to protect from high rainfall. In many places in the world unburnt mud-bricks are used where the rainfall is anything up to six times that of Mohenjo-daro. Conditions which all such places have in common would have been shared by the Indus Valley also, irrespective of the mean rainfall of the third millennium B.C. They all experience rain of high intensity that occurs in short periods separated by several days or weeks of dry conditions; and they all have the kind of climate in which the sun-drying of bricks is possible. In Baluchistan rainfall would have been, then as now, relatively higher than that of the Indus Valley for the background reasons given earlier; yet many of the Baluchistan chalcolithic cultures used sun-dried mud-bricks. It is not for me to say what made the Indus people use burnt bricks but I can at least hazard several guesses: desire for protection against the floods that are described in the next chapter; a tradition brought in from elsewhere; the technical ability to make burnt bricks and to appreciate that in the long-term they are economical; their advantage for multi-storey structures; the organising ability to produce bricks in quantity and cheaply.

The argument that a wetter climate would have been required to provide enough fuel does not hold good. Until recently, most main roads in the Indus Valley were paved with burnt bricks produced in enormous quantities locally. The fuel then used, and still used now, is tamarisk and *babul* (*Acacia arabica*) cut from the gallery forest along the river or from waste areas among the modern irrigations. These trees grow for the most part on shallow ground-water, and this must always have been present along the banks of the river. In the conditions of annual inundation that preceded the modern irrigation control of the Indus, the *Acacia arabica* probably flourished more than it does today as it benefits from being flooded annually.

However desert-like the land away from the main and flood channels of the ancient Indus happened to be, all these channels would have been marked by more or less dense gallery forest. It is difficult now, when seeing the apparently endless irrigated cultivation, to picture what the Indus was like before the barrages and canals were built. From the nature of the soils, however, one can guess that the ancient river meandered through a vast, almost bare, alluvial plain carrying only a sparse vegetation of typical desert plants such as camel thorn and possibly bunch grasses and occasional stunted acacia. On both sides of the river there must have been a strip of gallery forest whose width, density, and composition would vary according to the distance from the river, shading more or less rapidly through savanna-like conditions to desert vegetation. We do not know whether the Indus people practised large-scale seasonal irrigation by diverting and retaining part of each annual flood, or whether they were limited to use of the *shaduf*, the primitive device for lifting water that is still used along the Nile and in Mesopotamia and is pictured on Indus seals. They could have simply depended on cultivating the soil exposed by the receding flood, supplemented by primitive lift irrigation using the *shaduf* from small spur channels cut into the banks. Nothing in this tentative reconstruction is inconsistent with the availability of fuel.

The evidence of the drains at Mohenjo-daro is interesting because it illustrates the danger of not verifying each step in a process of reasoning. Drains normally serve one or both of two purposes. They may be required to carry away kitchen refuse, excreta, and dirty water, in which case they are specifically soil sewers: they may be required to carry away storm water as storm sewers: or they may serve both purposes. Drains or sewers used exclusively for the removal of soil sewage are always comparatively small, and all the more so in the absence of abundant piped-in water for baths, toilets, and so on. The size of storm sewers depends on the materials used for their construction, on the slope available and the type of storm that they have to cope with. The mean rainfall of a town has no bearing whatever on the design of its storm sewers. Their capacities depend primarily on the intensity and duration of storms on the area to be drained, and these can certainly be as high, and sometimes much higher, in arid than in temperate conditions.

The drains at Mohenjo-daro would be quite inadequate as storm drains today, and it is therefore reasonable to infer that they were not used for this purpose when the city was inhabited. On the other hand, their mere existence suggests water-borne sewerage and they deserve further study. It may be that the inhabitants made provision for flushing them of which the evidence has not survived or has not yet been correctly interpreted. There seems little doubt that they were intended as soil drains from the evidence of sundry small tributary drains, leading from individual buildings; it also seems certain that they served their purpose, for they were rebuilt at successive levels. It is inconceivable that the inhabitants should have relied on the very occasional storm to flush them. Perhaps a clue may be found in the outlets from numerous prehistoric loos that are not connected to the drains. These suggest the possibility that there may have been a regular sanitary service with water containers (perhaps on ox-carts) for the regular flushing down of both streets and drains: otherwise one is tempted to believe that their development of the indoor loo may have contributed to the disappearance of the civilisation. Whatever the purpose of these drains and however they were cleaned and flushed, they are not evidence of climate.

A case of a different kind is that of Pirak, a mound of an unknown but possibly very early period, near Sibi. In this case I appear to be the only person guilty of building a pyramid of speculation on inadequate data. If my tentative ideas of the date of the site—based on startling similarities between its pottery and a part of the ceramic assemblage of Samarra—are right, it might possibly be rash to claim that the climate has not changed at all: for residual ice-age glaciation on the Hindu Kush and Himalaya might have caused a somewhat different circulation pattern with more winter rain. However that may be, Pirak's situation in a rain-shadow from everywhere except the south would have ensured that any difference was small. The problem is to explain why such an uninviting place should have been occupied at all. The Kacchi Plain in summer is just about as horrible a place as it is possible to imagine. It is a vast, almost flat expanse of glaring mud, with summer temperatures that regularly reach 55°C. In the drainage lines some grasses and camel-thorn survive on the water absorbed during the passage of infrequent floods from the surrounding hills. Most of the time the flanking mountains are invisible in a haze of dust and when they do appear they do nothing to soften the landscape. However, not very far from Pirak is the present flood channel of the Nari river which drains a large area of the Baluchistan highlands and which occasionally delivers flood water to the Indus more than 200 kilometres away.

But how could such a large site—for it is some 400 ×300 metres—depend on these irregular floods? The answer is that the conditions at Pirak have been fundamentally changed by man. A barrage on the Nari river, north of Sibi where it flows perennially, diverts all the fairly considerable perennial flow for irrigation, while rough diversion banks on the Talli river, also perennial, ensure that none of its water reaches the Nari except during floods. It is almost certain that the Nari was perennial at least as far as Pirak before the construction of the barrage, and as there is no shortage of soil the essential requirements of the inhabitants could have been satisfied. That does not explain why the inhabitants chose to live in such a hot climate, but the example of modern Dhadar only a few miles away shows that great heat is not necessarily a discouragement. Sibi, much larger than Dhadar, is closer but owes its existence and importance to the railway.

Another example of the value of objective environmental studies could be provided by the Roman *limes* in North Africa and the Middle East. It is often said that North Africa, and particularly Cyrenaica, was the granary of Italy in Roman times, but climatic inferences from this overlook the political factors that depressed farming on mainland Italy to the benefit of overseas colonies. Cyrenaica today has a climate that could permit the cultivation of most of the crops and fruits that one finds in southern Italy. In Roman times it was certainly more productive than it is today, owing to efficient organisation and not only the construction, but the maintenance, of small dams and thousands of cisterns. The *limes*, with its system of closely spaced garrisons, was a political frontier and its establishment between the desert and the sown was a political necessity that had to be met irrespective of the climate. Many modern desert-fringe outposts are, for the same reasons, sited in unattractive places where water is difficult to obtain. Most, if not all, of the Roman outposts are in places where a similar political need could be as easily met today. There is no reason to suppose that the Romans were less hardy, adaptable, and resourceful in difficult conditions than people are now.

All the examples quoted so far are of the nature of critical reviews of the opinions and interpretations of others. The constructive aspect of these case studies, the hypothesis that conditions were no different from the widely variable ones of today, has not been stressed because it has already been stated earlier. If, however, a new approach to prehistory is to justify itself it must do more than demolish existing beliefs. For a long time there was so much to be reviewed that there was little time to develop a more original approach. The opportunity came when I was asked to prepare a paper for delivery to the Anthropological Society of Italy on any subject dealing with environment and human settlement in the past. The wide terms of reference were a positive handicap. Searching frantically for a useful theme, I drew a sketch of the Middle East, showing the modern rainfall isohyets as these seemed to be an obvious environment indicator in the geographical area that interested me most. Still with little notion beyond a wish to clarify my own ideas, I added to the sketch points showing various prehistoric sites. It was quickly obvious that the distribution of sites of a certain period—the early Neolithic—showed a correlation with rainfall distribution that could surely not be accidental. The rainfall data on which I based the isohyets were originally very patchy and sometimes of doubtful quality: the best of it was based, and much still is, on very small-scale isohyetal maps that gave no idea at all of local variations. However, as more data came in and I was able to pinpoint a few more sites, a fairly clear pattern began to emerge.

Mesolithic settlement sites were distributed in a fairly random manner above a certain isohyet. Early Neolithic sites, with very few exceptions, fell between two isohyets. Chalcolithic sites were again distributed randomly with penetration into drier areas. The two isohyets bracketing the early Neolithic sites were those of 300 mm. and 500 mm. The very little available data suggests that dry-farmed barley, that is, barley grown without benefit of any form of irrigation, requires a mean rainfall of about sixteen inches per annum or 400 mm.

From this emerged the idea, already described, of a free-ranging Mesolithic people forming rare settlements based on hunting and food-gathering; of an early Neolithic people exchanging mobility for the security of more regular food, initially from regular harvesting and later from cultivating the ancestors of our cereals and pulses; and finally of chalcolithic people, with knowledge of primitive irrigation and better cultivation techniques, capable of settling outside the restricted Neolithic habitat and spreading along river lines and up into rainier hill country. The maps shown as Pls. 10, 13, and 14 illustrate this idea. Mesolithic settlements would have been sited where game or some natural fruit or berry was abundant, and near water: there could have been seasonal hunting camps in the desert but settlements would have to be near an assured water supply. Neolithic settlements strung out along the narrow isohyetal strip shown in Pl. 14 would perforce have developed in a considerable degree of isolation—and perhaps at widely different times. In the chalcolithic period the ability to choose from a wider range of habitats would have started a new mobility with increasing cultural contacts.

If the theory was well-founded it could be important as supporting the proponents of parallel development during the early Neolithic beginnings of settled agriculture. It could also help us to find new sites of the Mesolithic-Neolithic transition by reducing the area of search. For in addition to the basic requirements of soil to cultivate and an assured water supply, only a place having rainfall of around 400 mm. per annum would qualify. Obviously there are exceptions, such as Jericho with about 170 mm., but there, as already mentioned, the great spring of 'Ain es Sultan is probably the explanation.

It seemed worthwhile putting the idea to a preliminary test, which I did in Jordan. First the modern 300 mm. and 500 mm. isohyets were located on the map, and then two of the wadis draining to the Jordan valley from the hills on the east bank were explored. A proper exploration would have required more time than I had available, so two wadis with roads were selected and only the fairly short inter-isohyetal strip explored on foot. In Wadi Sh'aib the 400 mm. isohyet coincided with large numbers of caves of an inconclusive nature: many waste flakes of flint suggested habitation and potsherds suggested a long occupation. However, these may have belonged to any period and the caves may have been occupied throughout by semi-nomadic elements. The inhabitants could have been interested in collecting wild cereals but there is no evidence to support this. A small mound at the 300 mm. isohyet on a cultivable alluvial terrace yielded a few rather inconclusive flint implements and a surprisingly wide range of potsherds. Nothing could be deduced from it.

In Wadi Kufrein, however, where there is much more cultivable terrace land and the other requirement of perennial wadi flow (as well as a small spring), there was quite a large site exactly on the 400 mm. isohyet. It was found entirely by searching the ground in the area already selected because whatever mound there may once have been has now been eroded away. A talus of typical mound debris, on the slope leading to the Wadi far below, suggests that there was a mound. A large area was thickly strewn with microliths and some larger blades: one tanged end of a broken blade recalled a similar object from pre-pottery Jericho. None of the large surrounding area yielded anything of interest and the concentration of microliths in one area certainly suggests a settlement. I know, as does anyone familiar with Jordan, that one cannot walk far over its hills and fields without finding some flint implements, but only in two other places had I found similar concentrations. All three were sites that had not been previously reported.

The existence of the Wadi Kufrein site at the point where theory suggested there should be one may be pure coincidence, but it certainly does not contradict the theory that there is a correlation between rainfall distribution and that of early prehistoric sites.

12 CASES INVOLVING HYDROLOGY AND GEOMORPHOLOGY

Most of the cases with which I have been concerned have involved not only hydrology and its climatic implications but also and at the same time the hydrological aspects of geomorphology. My division of them into two groups, climatic and geomorphological, is not intended to be arbitrary. I would prefer to emphasise the close inter-relationship of the two rather than their difference, although there is one distinct way in which the two groups differ: in the climatic group of studies the emphasis has been mainly on rainfall, while the studies now described are rather more concerned with flowing water and the material that it transports and deposits. They are of archaeological relevance because they have a bearing on why ancient cities were sited where they were, and sometimes on the way in which they came to an end; and on how ancient man created or preserved soil and irrigated it.

The *gabarbands* have already been dealt with in their role of witnesses for or against climate change. A brief description of how they were built and used can round off their story in this chapter. The traditional method of flood irrigation all over Baluchistan is known as *sailaba* and appears to be the lineal descendant of the method used by the builders of *gabarbands*. Nowadays a shallow impounding basin is constructed beside a normally dry torrent bed by scraping up whatever material is available to form the banks. The latter are L-shaped in plan with one arm running parallel and close to the torrent bed and the other running roughly at right-angles away from it. As the banks are built up to roughly the same level throughout their length, their height above ground is least upstream and increases steadily in a downstream direction, because of the longitudinal slope of the torrent, to a maximum at the point where the bank turns. From here the height of the bank above the ground decreases as the natural ground rises away from the torrent. The material is often initially the gravel or boulder alluvium of the torrent bed. A short spur bank of the same construction, sometimes stabilised with stakes, is built out into the stream bed in order to divert a part of any flood into the large shallow pocket formed by the *sailaba* banks. In the more evolved systems the spur bank delivers water into a feeder channel that may supply a series of *sailabas*. As initially built they leak like sieves, but as their object is to trap soil and not water this does not matter. Whatever the leakage, the velocity of water is much reduced so that at this early stage only suspended clay leaks away with the water. In time the banks and the bed of the basin become more or less sealed so that all the sediment is trapped. At this stage the water may take some time to evaporate or leak slowly away, but the beginnings of a field have been created in which the water stored in the soil is available for crops. The depth of clayey silt in some old *sailaba* fields can reach several metres. When the whole capacity of the basin is filled with soil the banks are generally raised a little, using the deposited impermeable material and from then on the flood water is used only to irrigate the field.

The sediment load of a flood varies considerably during the course of the flood and is often at a maximum (in the terms of percentage of the volume of water) at a fairly early stage and again at the extreme end of the flood recession. At such times the water can seem almost like liquid mud. Except during the process of forming a new *sailaba* terrace, a high sediment load is not only not needed but can do a lot of damage by burying seeds and seedlings under mud. Mature *sailaba* terraces generally far outnumber those that are being built up, which is just as well for it is easier to skim off a little flood-water at high stages then to divert even a part of the full depth of flow. Cultivators who use *sailaba* show considerable skill in selecting the kind of flood-water (with either more or less sediment) that they need.

The *gabarbands* often show unmistakable evidence of the L-shaped form typical of modern *sailaba* and often the remains of the silt trapped by them can still be identified. Like their modern counterparts, they must have leaked like sieves to start with, although their constructors must almost certainly have piled gravel against the upstream surface for otherwise they would not have held water long enough to make siltation effective. Once abandoned they have very little effect on the geomorphology of the valleys that contain them as they can only receive water when man intentionally diverts it to them. In this respect they do not at all resemble erosion control terraces.

Terraces of a rather similar kind seem to have been used by the Nabataeans in Jordan both for flood irrigation from normally dry wadis and for perennial irrigation from springs. The number of unmistakable flood irrigation structures that I have seen is, however, very small. Those used for perennial irrigation are necessarily fairly few for there is little perennial water. But the country to the north of Petra and Wadi Musa is very extensively terraced for what must have been largely soil erosion control, and for conservation of the low rainfall in terrace storage. These terraces are still in sufficiently good condition to exercise a considerable control over erosion, and in certain narrow alluvial valleys between masses of steep rock they appear to absorb very effectively the run-off concentrated on to them—for despite the very low rainfall crops are grown.

The Nabataean terraces, however, have an additional interest in providing an approximate *terminus ad quem* for the headward erosion of many of the wadis. The wadi that passes close to the prehistoric site of Beidha is a case in point. Downstream from the prehistoric site the wadi bed has reached bed-rock, but the evidence of Roman or Nabataean rock-cut tanks connected to the wadi show that it had already cut down to bed-rock some 2,000 years ago. Upstream from the site, although down-cutting has not reached bed-rock, it has progressed little in those 2,000 years for there are still Roman or Nabataean training walls at wadi level. Here and there where terraces have collapsed erosion is proceeding rapidly.

The geomorphology of the valley is of great interest. The site of Beidha is on an alluvial terrace remnant that agrees roughly for level and slope with other terrace remnants for several kilometres downstream to where a local erosional base-level is provided by a sheer drop of several hundred metres. Geological opinion is that successive down-faultings in this area have facilitated headward erosion, causing rejuvenation of valleys which had previously been filled with alluvium and were stable. A very rough calculation on the basis of a few flood observations, some rainfall intensity data, and estimates of long-term total run-off and sediment load, show that the amount of alluvial valley-fill removed by floods could be accounted for by some 9,000 years of the type and frequency of floods experienced today, operating in pre-Nabataean conditions without terrace protection. I do not say that it was removed in this period, but that it could have been without assuming improbable parameter values. The period would go back to about 2,000 years before the date of abandonment of the Neolithic site, but it is probable that headward erosion had by that time already reached far enough upstream to alter the run-off and ground-water régime at the site. Headward erosion in old valley-fill generally follows a dendritic pattern of which the main stem and the various branches reach their upstream limits long before erosion is complete. The explanation, in terms of down-faulting or tilting or relative movement of adjacent geological formations, of why the original alluvium extended down to, or possibly beyond the point where there is now a drop of several hundred metres, is a matter for the geologist. Whatever the explanation, it is fairly clear from the evidence that, at one time, the few kilometres of valley below Beidha were filled with deep alluvial material. Even the low rainfall of today could possibly have resulted in some intermittent surface flow in the wadi, particularly at points where the valley is constricted, as happens just below Beidha. In such circumstances there would have been both surface water and soil. It is impossible, however, to be certain that such were the conditions during the occupation of the site, for the erosion of the valley-fill may already have been completed in a far earlier epoch.

Recent erosion would not only provide an explanation of the otherwise almost inexplicable siting of Beidha, but it would also agree with the evidence afforded on the one hand by stability of the alluvial material where the Nabataeans terraced it, and of active erosion where their terraces have been destroyed.

If the event that started erosion occurred during the Neolithic occupation the main erosion stem would soon have created a gully. Long before the gully reached Beidha, the improved drainage provided by it would have converted any small sustained flow to intermittent floods which would themselves have accelerated the erosional process. The existing springs high up on the escarpment above Beidha, which are now partly used for local irrigation of small terraced fields, may provide a clue. Local people say that until quite recently the water from them flowed on the surface to a low level, and vegetation indicates that there is still some subsurface flow: the reduction of surface flow is probably due to the present irrigation use. Surface and subsurface flow, that originally reached the gently sloping and relatively impermeable valley-fill, would have created a water-body whose level would have depended on the downstream drainage base-level. If this were once high, both a shallow water table and intermittent surface flow would have been virtually certain.

A case, again from Jordan, of a quite different kind is that of a small site that I found south of Jurf ed Darwish and near the new desert highway. Originally I thought I had found a *tell* for it was the irregular mound shape, and its lack of conformity with its surroundings, that led me to it. The mound is littered with flint blades of every size, from large leaf-shaped highly patinated ones of Clactonian type to tiny microliths. There are also a few blades, having the original cortex as backing, that resemble Neolithic material (it does not follow that they were Neolithic). A Palaeolithic occupation mound associated with the large flakes that showed clactonian technique is obviously inconceivable: even a Mesolithic settled occupation associated with the microliths seems highly improbable. A Neolithic site could be explained in terms of climate change but it would not account for a preponderance of Palaeolithic material on the same site. Although no excavation has been carried out, the adjacent wadi has exposed a face of aclyey-silt material with approximately horizontal bedding and the surface distribution of Palaeolithic material suggests that much of it comes from the lower levels. Microliths occur for the most part where the silty material merges into gravel alluvium at the upstream end; that is where, perhaps, the silt tapers out over the gravel.

The explanation is a rather strange one. There are the very weathered remnants of a lava flow from the west that crossed or partly crossed the wadi and now stops just short of it at the downstream end of the site. It seems that this lava must at some time have created a dam behind which silt-laden water was impounded whenever an occasional flood occurred. Eventually the dam was breached and what we now see are the remains of the deposited silt. Any such seasonal pond in such a dry area would have been a focus for hunters or herders during the whole of its existence. Palaeolithic man probably came to drink and hunt the possibly large game that also drank there. Mesolithic man with his microlithic implements may have been more interested in duck-shooting. Neolithic man, provided occasionally with a large expanse of shallow water and much mud, may even have cultivated on the latter. In any case it was not an occupation site in the accepted sense.

The site of Yarim Tepe in Iran on the plains to the south-east of the Caspian may represent a reversal of the process that seems to have occurred at Beidha. The mound stands on a great expanse of plain that is drained by meandering streams flowing to the Caspian. The lowest occupation levels are a couple of metres or so below the plain level, while the adjacent stream bed is incised to some 10 metres below the same level. The photographs in Pls. 15 and 16 show the Tepe and the adjacent river. The depth of the stream bed seems to be greater than present flood discharge would account for, and so the present incised flood plain is probably the result of regular flows and a change in drainage base-level. Whatever the reasons for it, there seems to be little doubt that the level of the Caspian Sea has been steadily falling and that the consequent lowering of the drainage base-level accounts for the depth of incision. The very considerable capacity of this deeply incised channel makes it unlikely that floods could overflow on to the plain. If, very rarely, they have done so it hardly accounts for the difference between the old and the present flood-plain levels. It could have been so but is the least probable of several alternatives which should all be borne in mind.

One possible alternative is shown by the geological map of the area on which are indicated mud volcanoes on a south-west to north-east line between Yarim Tepe and the Caspian, transverse to the general drainage direction. So-called volcanic mud can be extruded through vents resembling volcanoes, or massively along fault-lines, or both, and in either case is invariably associated with a fault or faults. If such faults are active the crustal movement associated with them can cause surface movement and either tilting or local block movement up or down. Any mud extruded to the surface or intruded under shallow alluvium can cause changes of surface level. It is possible that something of this kind created a raised terrace or a low barrier between Yarim Tepe and the Caspian and altered the régime of the river, either by changing its gradient or by creating a low dam. Either way, silt-laden flood water would have overflowed and, by depositing its silt, raised the level of the plain. Subsequent cutting of the barrier would have restored the original river-bed gradient. Whether either of these possibilities is of archaeological significance can only be decided by Dr Stronach who excavated the site and with whom I spent three busy and interesting days seeing it, the Belt Cave, one or two other sites, and the incredibly beautiful country of the northern Elburz.

The new road to the Caspian over the Elburz mountains skirts around the foot of Demavend, which at that point is nearly 14,000 feet above the level of the road itself. It is splendid country, mostly very stark and arid until the general slope to the northward is established well to the north of Demavend. Even on this northward general slope, dense vegetation is not met until quite near the level of the Caspian plain where first beeches and then oaks occur as thick forest. The contrast between aridity and snow drifts at the top and primroses and oak forest near the plain is that between two utterly different worlds.

Study of the boulder alluvium terraces in the valley that follows the road could perhaps contribute valuable information for the problem of Caspian Sea levels. The topographic and hydrologic data available to me are practically non-existent, so

15. This small river passes close to Yarim Tepe in Iran near the Caspian and has cut into a part of the ancient mound (on left).

16. This view, looking upstream, suggests two distinct down-cutting phases both of which have occurred since the earliest occupation of the site. The lowest levels of Yarim Tepe are just below the lower terrace level. It follows that the general flood plain level has been created since that time and subsequently cut down by the river.

17. (*Above*) Sterile silty-clay material at Mohenjo-daro. The thickness and composition of the material as well as the laminations discernible under close examination indicate that deposition occurred under still-water conditions. Care is needed to distinguish this material from mud-brick which was extensively used for massive filling operations. The deposit pictured is at some 7 or 8 metres above the present flood-plain level.

18. (*Left*) Typical occupation debris containing sherds, stones, etc., and with sub-horizontal and sometimes cross-bedded stratification: for comparison with 14. The example pictured is from Tell es Sultan, Jericho.

it would be irresponsible to try to recreate the conditions of alluviation and down-cutting. The problem is of particular interest because the normal arid-zone conditions, of decreasing rainfall with decreasing altitude, are reversed. Here the high mountains are arid and the low valleys towards the Caspian enjoy not only much higher rainfall but also the absence of a very long summer drought.

The way in which valley-fill could be built up in such conditions would depend on many factors such as the seasonal snow-melt from the high mountains and the seasons (if any) of high intensity rainfall in the low valley. The deep incision of former very deep valley-fill that has left only a few terrace remnants suggests that a change of drainage base-level—such as a lowering of Caspian sea-level—must have occurred, but it is impossible to be certain.

Other studies in the hydro-geomorphological class have concerned floods. I will restrict myself to two on which I have worked with archaeologists: Sybaris in southern Italy, and Mohenjo-daro in West Pakistan. At Sybaris, or what is believed to be the site of that city, three or four years of investigations had already yielded a mass of factual data by the time that I became involved. The data had been collected by the Museum of the University of Pennsylvania and the Fondazione Lerici, working in collaboration with the local Soprintendenza alle Antichità. Originally invited to advise on the dewatering of the excavations which had defied normal pumping methods, I became involved in a general investigation through a quick scrutiny of some plotted bore-hole data. These showed rather surprisingly that the bottom of the clay of the flood plain of the rivers Crati and Coscile becomes not only deeper from the surface as one proceeds inland (which is not surprising) but that its level relative to the sea also gets lower. They also showed—a fact that I had not originally appreciated—that both the archaic and hellenistic artifacts brought up by drilling came from well below sea-level. The dates ascribed to such materials are between about the eighth and third centuries B.C.

I have already given general reasons for doubting that general ocean levels have changed more than a few centimetres in the last 6,000 years. In the case of Sybaris, there exist more

13

precise reasons for doubting this. At Metaponto, not far away to the north-east, the ruins of a Greek coastal city of about the same period are now above sea-level: at Paestum, to the north on the Tyrrhenian sea coast, a Greek coastal city is believed to have been submerged by the sea, and subsequently to have re-emerged, since its occupation. It is obviously not the sea that has changed level in relation to the land, but vice versa.

According to legend, Sybaris met its end at the hands of the rival city of Crotone whose army diverted the waters of the river and flooded and destroyed the city. Like most legends it probably contains a grain, or in this case a droplet, of truth, for the situation of Sybaris below sea-level does immediately suggest that water was involved in its destruction. The rest of the legend is of course pure moonshine. During the winter or after unpredictable summer floods the Crati or Coscile could not possibly be dammed by primitive methods: it would be difficult and costly even with modern methods. The quite unpredictable duration of low flows would have made its damming at such times a hazardous affair that would have taken many months to complete merely within the channel itself and, unless the dam were continued for some kilometres laterally on the side away from Sybaris, there would have been only a remote chance that the diverted water of the next flood would affect the city at all. As all this is said to have been done after the city had already been defeated it seems an unnecessary amount of trouble.

What seems more probable is that a close conjunction in time of the conquest of Sybaris and a natural disaster that submerged its ruins grew into the legend as we know it.

At Sybaris, all the hundreds of bore-hole records were made available to me. The records were not on the whole bore-hole logs in the accepted sense, and the method of drilling was aimed rather at obtaining a mass of data quickly (and very successfully) than at getting precise information. The stratigraphy of artifacts found in the clay, resulting from this method, gave a good idea of the sequences and a fair idea of the depths. But what every sufficiently deep hole gave with considerable accuracy was the level of the horizon between the clay of the flood plain and the underlying sand. Good aerial mapping provided reliable ground levels and it was possible to plot with some confidence the topography of the underlying sand.

This produced a really rather dramatic result. All the main concentrations of artifacts and all the structures revealed by geophysical methods were on, or at the edges of, a series of buried sand-dunes running roughly parallel with the present coast. Other secondary concentrations of potsherds were mainly at considerable depth at the bottom of the overlying clay on the inland side of the dunes. Some were also on the seaward side but covered smaller areas nearer to the dunes. The tendency for the bottom of the clay to slope downwards inland, seen during the first scrutiny of a few bore-holes, was confirmed. So, assuming that general sea-level was no different then from what it is now, which seems reasonable in the context of Metaponto, Paestum, and other places of the same period, it seems reasonable to infer that the land on which the city stood subsided several metres. If the dunes subsided, so did the clay plain on which they stood or the bed of the lagoon that lapped them. Either slowly or catastrophically the sea washed over the dunes. A catastrophic inrush of sea water would be more in line with the legend and would presumably have destroyed everything. A slow invasion would have been perhaps even more destructive over a long period during which every storm would have caused waves to pound away at the ruins. I prefer the catastrophic version for several reasons: the legend; the tendency of sherds to be washed inland; and particularly the tilt of the underlying sand which suggests either down-faulting or folding or some kind of slip phenomenon. If the tilt had occurred gradually, I suspect that the sand would have had time to adjust to the new level before deposits of clay sealed it into place.

The existence of a late Hellenistic settlement, itself below present sea-level, and the gap in time between the two settlements suggest that the creation of a more or less salt lagoon behind the dunes caused temporary water-supply problems. The later settlement would only have been possible if the first settlement had been left a little above sea-level, and this suggests the probability of a catastrophic subsidence accompanied by a tidal wave. The lagoon would gradually have become cleared of sea-water and in time would have become silted, and the second settlement could have been helped by some fresh dune sand deposition over the old ruins or by some artificial raising of the level. As this second settlement is itself below sea-level whereas the succeeding Roman levels are not, it seems probable that another catastrophic or gradual subsidence took place, leaving only island remnants of the original dunes for the Romans. The construction by them of an aqueduct, to near the present bridge that carries the Strada Consorziale over the Crati, suggests perhaps a Roman island fort guarding the lagoon and river mouth; or even a more prosaic fishing village. We are sometimes a little prone to picture Romans as soldiers in picturesque armour or as lawmakers in flowing togas, and to forget that there was a multitude of farmers, fishermen, tradesmen, and labourers to supply their needs.

The investigations just described and the inferences drawn do not necessarily, even if they are right, help in unravelling the problem of Sybaris, but they do give an example of one of the more violent ways in which our environment can change the course of history.

As I was working on Mohenjo-daro and Sybaris more or less simultaneously, the differences in the two problems were heightened for me though they may not seem so obvious to others.

Mohenjo-daro was a capital city of the Indus Civilisation. Some would have it that it was one of twin capitals. I prefer to think it was the earlier and abandoned in favour of the other at Harappā. The site has been admirably described by others and particularly by Sir Mortimer Wheeler. Until recently, the evidence found by Sir John Marshall and later by Wheeler, of at least 10-metres depth of deposits below the level of the Indus flood plain, with some other direct archaeological evidence, was interpreted in terms of successive destruction of the city by abnormal flowing floods. The whole chain of reasoning and of the investigations carried out would take too long to tell here. The evidence does not come only from the Indus Valley but also from Baluchistan and from the Arabian Sea coast in Mekran and Bela, where settlements of the Indus people have been found. As I merely want to use this story as an illustration of a type of problem, only a condensed account is given here.

I was never particularly happy at the idea of such an enormous depth of flood silt having been built up even in the whole period of some 4,400 years since the date ascribed to the beginnings of the city. It is conceivable but improbable. What could not be accepted was the feasibility of the deposition of some 150–200 centimetres of silt in a single flood episode, for it implied the simultaneous deposition of something like this depth over an area of thousands of square kilometres. For this, and some smaller but still considerable depths of silt, is the evidence of the tentative stratigraphy reconstructed by Stuart Piggott. Briefly, it was believed that between about 2400 B.C. and 1500 B.C. a series of disastrous floods occurred at long intervals, each partially submerging the city and the surrounding countryside under great depths of flood silt. Each successive reconstruction was founded on the buried ruins of its predecessor. There are two grave objections to this view. One, which can be called the common-sense one easily appreciable by any layman, is that it requires acceptance of a succession of disasters during a comparatively short period of 900 years and nothing during the succeeding 3,400 years. This is improbable to say the least of it. The second is that suspended sediment occupies a minute fraction of the volume of water transporting it—far less than one per cent in a river like the Indus—and that only a small part of the silt is deposited unless the water is stagnant. The depth of even slowly flowing water that would be required to deposit these vast depths of silt over vast areas would require not a flood but a slowly moving inland sea. Even if parts of a city survived, its inhabitants would inevitably have gone to feed the sharks in the Arabian Sea.

On examination of the flood deposits it was found that they are not of silt but of silty-clay which behaves quite differently. Silt can be deposited from flowing water; clay only from still water. Measurements of the levels of flood deposits showed how difficult it must have been for Professor Piggott to make any sense out of excavation data, for they occur at almost every level *above* the ground and probably follow a similar random pattern throughout. The fact that the deposits occur above present ground level seems at first to complicate the issue, but it helped very much in arriving at a rational, but not necessarily correct, solution. It seems to complicate it because the visual identification of flood deposits up to some 10 metres above the plain, and the discovery by drilling that they go down to at least 12 metres below, meant that the total depth of deposits is 22 metres. At this depth any idea of deposition under flowing water, over a period of a few hundred years, must be abandoned.

The solution that has been put forward as a result of recent studies depends basically on evidence of uplift along the Mekran coast; on the assumption that the silty-clay must have been deposited under still water conditions; and on the historical case of the Allah Band on the north of the Rann of Kutch. The latter achieved news value recently as the site of a border dispute. Early in the last century Allah Band suddenly appeared as the result of some unidentified tectonic activity accompanied, not unnaturally, by an earthquake. Its great length and considerable height dammed a part of the Indus, creating a lake 5,000 square kilometres in area, that took two years to dissipate. A clue to the cause of this uplift was afforded by the appearance in 1945 of two small islands off Pasni, attributed to eruptive mud volcanoes. There is much evidence of mud eruption along the Arabian Sea coast.

It seems inescapable that an event or series of events such as that at Allah Band, and probably due to intruded volcanic mud, dammed the Indus. Suitable geological formations exist near Sehwan which is therefore the most likely site of the dam. The erupted mud forcing up the original fine sand, with its thin original cover of alluvial sandy-clay, of the Indus Valley formed a highly permeable sand dam inadequately waterproofed by the thin layer of clay. Drilling at Mohenjo-daro revealed this fine sand a couple of metres only below the lowest occupation level and its thin clay covering on which the lowest level was built. Being permeable, the dam permitted the leakage of Indus water but created still water conditions under which the whole of its sediment load was deposited. As the waters, and mud, gradually rose they would have overwhelmed, one after another, the Indus cities south of Mohenjo-daro and eventually reached that city. The approach of flood water slowly and inexorably from downstream would have given the inhabitants plenty of time to build the massive mud-brick platforms that have been found at various levels and to raise their houses. This successive raising of house walls is one of the strangest things about Mohenjo-daro and is very simply explained in this way.

It seems probable that the rise of water level occupied the whole of the so-called mature phase of the city. I would guess that it could have taken 100 years from the uplift event, and much less than that time to account for the 22 metres at Mohenjo-daro itself. Ultimately, when the 'reservoir' was full, a flood must have overflowed the bank and started headward erosion. This, sooner or later, exposed the part of Mohenjo-daro that is now above the plain.

I believe that some parts of the city had been abandoned before the flood reached its full height, but that a nucleus survived that served to recolonise the abandoned parts as they emerged. A flood of this kind would have destroyed the gallery forest and the re-erosion would have delayed its re-establishment. This may be a reason for an apparent lack of new burnt bricks in the later periods.

The problem is considerably more complicated than appears from this brief account which is given mainly to show that evidence of floods requires very careful interpretation.

In closing I will give one more example of the need for objective specialist advice.

I mentioned earlier the case of Petra. The ruins of the Nabataean and Roman cities are hidden away in a remote valley almost surrounded by precipitous sandstone rocks, and reached by a long extremely narrow chasm in the rocks known as the Siq. There are small springs within the city area and in the surrounding deep valleys: a little downstream from the city, Wadi Musa, now dry except in floods where it traverses the city, has perennial flow. The total of these sources of water fairly obviously did not suffice for the city's needs, for if so it is difficult to understand the reason for the rock-cut channels and remains of earthenware piping that seem to have served to bring water to it from upstream. Some kilometres upstream is the large spring of 'Ain Musa (alleged to be the spring that appeared when Moses struck the rock), and this was probably the supply point from which the channels led. It has been argued that the failure of the waters of 'Ain Musa to reach even the outskirts of Petra nowadays is due to the climate having become drier. This takes no account of what happens to the water now. It is all canalised and quite skilfully distributed to the terrace cultivations of the modern village. The site of the modern village, outside the impregnable area of Petra, would have been very vulnerable to raiders and hard to defend in Nabataean times, and there is no evidence of a Nabataean village there. Without the present diversion of the waters of 'Ain Musa these would almost certainly have reached at least as far as the upstream end of the ancient system of rock-cut channels which extends for a considerable distance above the Siq towards Wadi Musa village. Whatever changes have been wrought by climate, of which there is no direct evidence, the observed change is quite amply accounted for by present-day use of the water. At the entrance to the Siq the Romans constructed a diversion dam, *not* for storage of water, in conjunction with a really enormous diversion tunnel. The capacity of this is such that it seems probable that in Roman times flash floods were experienced as they are today.

EPILOGUE

13 THE INTERDISCIPLINARY APPROACH

It may be a truism to say that prehistory, history and life as we know it are all part of the same indivisible process of human social evolution but, if so, it is not by any means generally recognised.

Understanding of any part of the process is based on two main factors: the existence of evidence or data; and the ability to interpret them. This is so obviously true of life as we know it that many of us do not appreciate it. When we form a judgment or opinion from what we read in books or newspapers we are unconsciously interpreting from what we all too frequently take to be facts. We do the same when, within a profession or discipline, we marshal the facts and interpret them, generally with the help of what others have done before.

A thing that we are apt to overlook is the quite extraordinary extent to which we lack precise verifiable data in our everyday lives. Practically all our knowledge is gained at second hand through books, radio, television and newspapers. We think that we know what is happening today in another country whereas in fact our 'knowledge' is compounded of impressions, prejudices, occasional verifiable facts, and a mass of more or less subjective reporting. In most things that matter we either consciously check our knowledge by consulting different sources or we unconsciously assume that the checking has been done by others. For instance comparatively few have had occasion to verify for themselves Newton's First Law of Motion but we know that it has been verified by enough people, including initially many opponents of it, for us to be able to accept what it propounds as a fact for all normal purposes.

So present-day beliefs about matters of today are only very seldom entirely unrelated to verifiable basic data; and irrational belief generally afflicts only the lunatic fringes.

We have every reason, in our artificial and complex lives that leave us little enough time for original or creative thought, to refuse to waste the little time we have in verifying for ourselves what others have done satisfactorily for us. We have every reason to feel confidence in most of the deductions, conclusions and physical laws reached and propounded by others simply because the meretricious is quickly shown up in a literate society. A world in which no one could benefit from the accumulated knowledge of others would be an odd place even if it were spared some of the more gross misuses of knowledge such as napalm and nuclear weapons.

So we are, in the context of the present and the recent past, generally on safe ground in letting others do the hard deductive work.

In history which deals with events that may have happened only a few tens of generations ago, we seldom have the time and patience to study original data and indeed the amount of genuine original fact available is negligible. What we study are contemporary opinions and we do not always fully appreciate that both these and the views of modern historians that are based on them are inevitably subjective. If anyone doubts this let him read first an English and then a French version of Anglo-French relations in the Middle Ages; or the history of England as seen by the Danes. However the broad outlines of history generally emerge fairly unscathed simply because many original contemporary opinions are available to historians and published histories get rough treatment at the hands of the critics if they step too far out of line.

In the study of prehistory, in which we are by definition denied any written record however fallible or subjective, we are or should be constrained to use consciously all the many disciplines whose contributions we use consciously or unconsciously in our everyday lives. Data are so scarce in any one field that deductions from them are really more of the nature of speculations. It is from a realisation of this that the present tendency towards an interdisciplinary approach originated. If the data in one field are insufficient, then the possibility of exploring other fields and of discovering some sort of convergence of results is the only hope.

The complexity of even the simplest human societies is such that some degree of specialisation is essential. What started long ago as specialised skills in primitive societies have developed into the bewildering diversity of trades and disciplines of modern advanced societies. Their interdependence is at the root of social life, of which therefore the study is essentially interdisciplinary—or should be. Some prefer the word multidisciplinary though it seems regrettable that either of these ugly words should be preferred. As there seems to be no more euphonious alternative I prefer to settle for the first because it does infer collaboration while the second suggests an intellectual Tower of Babel.

Collaboration in archaeology is accepted in principle and sometimes practised but its results seem to indicate that something is wrong, and I do not think it is particularly difficult to identify this. To return to those ugly words I think that what we are seeing in operation is a multidisciplinary approach instead of an interdisciplinary one. Each specialist is working perhaps too much in his own field with the result that collaboration comes at too late a stage when conclusions have already become too rigid. Most facts, particularly when they are scarce, admit of quite a wide range of possible interpretations and unless one specialist's range is compared at an early stage with those of others the opportunity of correlation may be lost.

The too frequent use of such expressions as 'There can be no reasonable doubt that . . .' affords a clue and they should be ruthlessly expunged unless they are meticulously qualified as to the limited range of conditions in which they are true. It seems to me that the moment when the temptation to write such words arises is precisely the moment at which the conclusion to which they refer should be submitted to tests by others in other disciplines. I am not advocating a committee approach nor that of the 'working party' even when the latter, as does occasionally happen, forgets that it is a party and works. Both are time-consuming and mainly provide a forum for those who have little to say but the ability to say it convincingly. I do not even suggest that interdisciplinary teams must necessarily get together around a table. Even the worst postal services deliver the goods eventually and correspondence, even if it does not silence the demagogue, takes away most of his unfair advantage and gives time for thought. The ideal is for each specialist to work on his own but to submit his work to others for comment and criticism as every tentative conclusion is reached.

But this is only a part of what is needed. It is perhaps even more important that every specialist should seek the comments and criticisms of other workers in his own field before contributing his tentative conclusions to colleagues in other disciplines. Even those who are recognised as unusually competent in their chosen fields are not always right, and those who are brilliant are sometimes even more prone to error even if their genius can sometimes produce in a moment results that might involve the competent in years of patient work.

In the professions and in academic life the results of research are invariably submitted by their authors to debate or written discussion by other members of the same profession. The traditional archaeologist is no exception but a scientist working in archaeology tends to publish his conclusions in archaeological journals where they escape criticism by other workers in the same field of specialisation.

It is flattering for a scientist to be treated as if he were an oracle but he does not, or should not, enjoy the kind of diplomatic immunity enjoyed by the oracles of old and should always be ready to submit to the healthy restraint of criticism from his professional colleagues. We should remember that we are not experts but merely fortunate in possessing a little specialised knowledge in one small sector of life, whether that of today or that of several millennia ago. I hesitate even to use the word expert: it has become so debased through indiscriminate use.

It is much easier to suggest cures than to put them into effect. To ensure that scientific advice to archaeologists should be of all the right kinds and given only by those qualified to do so, involves initially persuading a sufficient number of active archaeologists that it is necessary. For where any excavation or exploration programme is undertaken the director is entirely and personally responsible, and rightly, for the choice of his team and his advisers and the idea of several experts on an overseas dig with limited funds would make any director quail. Even if a few leading archaeologists set an example by having all the necessary disciplines represented as advisers it simply would not be practicable for all to follow their example.

There is also the difficulty that sometimes the whole scope of studies necessary to determine the prehistoric environment at a site is not known until the dig or exploration has started and by then it is generally too late.

The only practical advice that I would offer is that archaeologists should either resist entirely the temptation to pronounce upon highly complex environmental matters or, in the rare cases where their interpretation is vital to a proper understanding of the site, make provision for proper specialist advice. It costs nothing to write and ask for a general opinion which would often be quite enough, but it does seem essential that somebody with a knowledge of rainfall, climate, run-off, and other hydrological factors should be among those approached.

Unfortunately exchanges of views, or the giving and taking of advice however willingly undertaken, cannot be effective unless the difficulty of communication is recognised and can be overcome. It is not merely the difficulty of communicating across disciplinary boundaries, which can be eased a little by avoiding jargon and, what is worse than jargon, the use of ordinary words in unusual senses. If one assumes, as it seems reasonable to do, that archaeological studies, financed often by public subscription or helped by government subventions, should not be purely academic exercises and that the results should be made available to as wide a public as possible, there is also the problem of communicating the results to that public.

I have been very much aware for a long time of the difficulty of crossing disciplinary boundaries and still have no clear idea of how to overcome it. In trying to communicate with the whole diverse range of persons, all interested in one way or another in archaeology, to whom this book is addressed, I have realised that the difficulty is even more formidable than I had thought. There may even be a hydrologist among them to whom my attempts to put things in simple language may seem an insult (apart from the risk that some of my hydrological opinions may seem to him to be heresy): there may be some to whom it will be a convenient soporific for a long flight or train journey and to whom therefore my success or lack of it in communication is of little importance. In between there could be all shades of knowledge, of fixed opinions, and of open-mindedness or prejudice. I know that some concepts that seem to me, from long familiarity with them, to be self-evident truth are either incomprehensible or nonsense or both to intelligent people whose opinions I value. Even when there is little technical barrier to understanding there is still an element of subjectivity.

On the other hand there is some comfort in knowing that these are difficulties that I share with all other writers and particularly with those who write about little-known subjects. So far as I have been able to discover no one has so far written a book in English devoted to the water and weather that prehistoric man enjoyed, or to which he submitted more or less philosophically. In a way this makes the task of writing more than usually daunting: but there is the consolation of hoping that it may stimulate a little interest, a little extension of the inter-disciplinary range; and, as a result, that it may help to solve, for future writers on this subject, some of the difficulties of communication by showing up where these are particularly acute.

I have sometimes perhaps seemed unduly critical of the scant attention paid until now to the scientific study of an essential part of prehistoric environment. If so it is really a criticism of the discipline that I profess for not having offered its services earlier. When prehistorians were first seeking help in environment studies some forty or fifty years ago hydrology was still groping around in an empirical blindfold and could not help, so they went to other professions. I have sometimes been even more critical of the answers given by other professions where they touch mine. This is inevitable and I make no apologies for it. When opinions have hardened into belief and both are based, even if only partly, on wrong premises it is not only legitimate but absolutely necessary to attack what one believes to be wrong. It is just as useless to propose new ideas without first demonstrating that the old ideas may be wrong as it is to attack old ideas without proposing anything in their place.

These new ideas must be viewed by others with as much scepticism as I have applied to the ideas that I do not agree with. Even though I am sincerely convinced of what I write I am even more convinced by the history of scientific advance that events may prove me wrong!

There is so much to be done, both in the field of prehistoric environment and in the interpretation of prehistoric structures for the control and use of water, that I hope others whose business it is to study water and its use may be encouraged to take a hand. Those who do so will get much of value in return, for archaeology can give perspective to the problems of today.

Acknowledgements

My thanks go first of all to my wife who has had the unrewarding task of checking and correcting my writing and of trying to represent the non-technical reader with whom I am trying to communicate. I hope that putting her first will make some amend for the grudging way in which many of her criticisms and suggestions have been accepted. It seems that teaching one's husband to write is as fraught with danger as teaching one's wife to drive a car.

Without active encouragement from many archaeological friends I would never have dared embark on this work. It may be invidious to select certain of them for individual mention but in some cases the debt is very great. So my particular thanks go to Professor Stuart Piggott who encouraged my first article; to Miss Beatrice de Cardi who helped to sustain my interest in ancient things; to Sir Mortimer Wheeler who has considered my ideas worthy of both trenchant criticism and support; and Professor Giuseppe Tucci who has encouraged their publication. The others include many good friends and colleagues of the University Museum in Philadelphia, the Directors and their staffs of many archaeological services in the Middle East, and the staffs of many museums and archaeological institutions.

Perhaps my greatest debt of all is to the late Professor F. E. Zeuner whose masterly synthesis in *Dating the Past* provided much material that could otherwise only have been available through years of concentrated research.

Last but not least are all those with whose views I have disagreed more or less profoundly. There is nothing so stimulating as a lively opposition.

Suggested Reading

GENERAL

A History of Domesticated Animals by F. E. Zeuner, Hutchinson, London, 1963.

Changes of Climate: Proceedings of the Rome Symposium organised by UNESCO and the World Meteorological Organisation, UNESCO, 1963.

Civilisations of the Indus Valley and Beyond, by Sir Mortimer Wheeler, Thames and Hudson, 1966.

Dating the Past, by F. E. Zeuner, 4th edition, Methuen, London, 1958.

Environment and Archaeology, by Karl W. Butzer, Methuen, London, 1965.

Habitat, Economy and Society, by C. Darryl Forde, Methuen, London, 1934.

Land behind Baghdad, by Robert McC. Adams, University of Chicago Press, 1965.

Prehistoric India, by Stuart Piggott, Penguin Books, Harmondsworth, 1950.

'Prehistoric Investigations in Iraqi Kurdistan', by R. Braidwood et al., *Studies in Ancient Oriental Civilisations*, Chicago, Vol. 31, 1960.

The Scientist and Archaeology, ed. E. Pyddoke, Phoenix House, London, 1963.

HYDROLOGY AND METEOROLOGY

A Course in Elementary Meteorology, Meteorological Office, H.M. Stationery Office, London, 1962.

Groundwater Hydrology, by David K. Todd, Wiley and Sons, London and New York, 1960.

Hydrologie de Surface, by M. Roche, Office de la Recherche Scientifique et Technique Outre-mer (Paris), Gauthier-Villars, Paris, 1963.

Hydrology, by C. O. Wisler and E. F. Brater, 2nd edition, Chapman and Hall, London, 1959.

Hydrology for Engineers, by Linsley, Kohler and Paulhus, McGraw-Hill, 1958.

Hydrology Handbook of the American Society of Civil Engineers.

Vegetation and Hydrology, by H. L. Penman, Technical Communication No. 53, Commonwealth Agricultural Bureaux, Farnham Royal, England.

The above are selected more or less at random from the very extensive literature on the subject.

Articles by the author that describe in detail the cases described in Chapters 11 and 12 and some others:

'A New Prehistoric Bichrome Ware from the Plains of Baluchistan': *East and West*, new series, Vol. 14, 1 and 2; Istituto per il Medio e Estremo Oriente, Rome, 1963.

'A Supplementary Note on Pirak Bichrome Ware': *East and West*, new series, Vol. 15, 1 and 2; Istituto per il Medio e Estremo Oriente, Rome, 1965.

'Physical Environment and Human Settlement in Prehistoric Times in the Near and Middle East. A Hydrological Approach': *East and West*, new series, Vol. 15, 3 and 4; Rome, 1965.

'Sites in Wadi Shu'eib and Kufrein, Jordan': *Palestine Exploration Quarterly*, July–December, 1965.

'The Ancient Gabarbands of Baluchistan': *East and West*, new series, Vol. 15, 1 and 2, Rome, 1965.

'The End of the Ancient Cities of the Indus': *American Anthropologist*, Vol. 66, No. 2, 1964.

'The Mohenjo-daro Floods': *Antiquity*, XXXIX, 1965.

'The Physical Evidence for Noah's Flood' *IRAQ*, June/July 1966.

'The Prehistoric Climate of Baluchistan and the Indus Valley' (jointly with Dr Robert H. Dyson, Jr.): *American Anthropologist*, Vol. 63, 1961.

GENERAL INDEX

TECHNICAL INDEX

(with rare exceptions limited to Chapters 1 to 8)